Christy:
It was good talking to you. You are a
special lady – even if you are a friend of Julies!

Blessings.

Don Bakely

Bethy and the Mouse

God's Gifts in Special Packages

Donald C. Bakely

Bethany
or Tagg
Bakely   I love
you

Library of Congress Number 85-70634
International Standard Book Number 0-87303-111-3
Printed in the United States of America
Copyright © 1985 by Faith and Life Press
718 Main Street, Newton, KS 67114

Photos by Terry Evans: pages 15, 22, 61, 93, 96, 100, 106, 116.

Design by John Hiebert
Printing by Mennonite Press, Inc.

This book is dedicated to:

- The God who was wise enough
                    to give us Beth
        at a time in our lives
            when we really
                would rather not have had
                                another child;

- Jeanne, my wife,
        whose special love,
            combined with her fears,
                            agonies,
                            and work,
        have helped so many of us
            to find an extra warmth
                        in our lives;

- Our other children,
                    Paul,
                    Steve,
                    Claudia,
                    Pete,
                    and Lois,
        whose immediate delight
                        over Beth's life,
        whose absolute acceptance,
            overpowering help,
            and constant love for Beth
                so beautifully lifted our spirits
                        and our load;

- The "Mouse" (our son, Matthew)
        who died before Beth was born,
        but who would have been delighted
                            with her company
                            and her antics;

• The gang at the Infant Development Center
        in Johnson County, Kansas,
    who not only saw who Beth *was*,
            but who she *could* be,
    who studied,
        trained,
        taught,
        opened doors,
        pushed,
        encouraged,
        and loved Beth,
    and who lifted, taught, and encouraged us as a family;

• And to the rest of us on God's earth
    who find ourselves retarded
        in the love we give
        and the accomplishments we would like to achieve,
    yet attempt to grow more
        in what we give to others
    and realize that we, too, are special
        and have special gifts yet to offer
                    to those in need.

Foreword

How brief is the time from diapers to kindergarten! The years have passed so swiftly since we first met Bethany.

How well I remember her dear daddy, Don, sheltering her in his large hands. How tiny she was as she and her parents entered our world at the Infant Development Center in Shawnee Mission, Kansas, five years ago. Four weeks of age and eight pounds of dynamite—none of us knew yet how our lives would intertwine.

Jeanne—a super mom! So sweet, so steady, so helpful to the other moms, yet hurting so inside for her little daughter.

Don—an inspiration to all—so strong—so vivacious— so deep and caring, not only for Bethany but for all the other children, too.

Bethany—a tiny rosebud of a person who gazed intently at us all. She would never know the concern we felt. She was so frail and gained so slowly.

There is no more exciting adventure than to join hands with a family and fight together for the life and the future of their little child. We crawled inside each other, we cried together, and we embraced each other in joy with each step forward.

A label—Down's syndrome—can say so much, yet so little. The label says retarded, slow, floppy, dull, different, special education. "They" said it couldn't be done. At times *we* said it couldn't be done. But Beth seemed to say, "Look at me. I'm a person. Let me try. I can do it!"

When her medical chart said, "Failure to thrive," we worried.

When she reached out and pulled her daddy's beard, we laughed.

When she walked alone, we cheered.

When she called pancakes, "cake cakes," we laughed.

When she threw a tantrum like any other two-year-old, we quietly cheered.

When she called herself, "Beckany Blecklick," so did we.

When she entered the mainstreamed preschool, we prayed.

When she passed the entrance exam for kindergarten, we told everyone we knew about it.

And when she hugged us for the last time on her graduation day, we were devastated, but oh, so proud!

The Infant Development Center and Preschool serves developmentally disabled children between birth and five years of age. We offer therapy and education to children, and support and information to parents. The staff includes a program director, registered physical therapists, speech pathologists, early childhood education teachers, and a pediatric consultant. The pediatrician examines each child, counsels with parents, reports to primary physicians, and serves as advisor to the staff.

Treatment, home programs, and parent groups are an ongoing process as staff and family work together with and for each child. The children are evaluated by the team every six months, and a conference is held with the family so that the Individual Program Plan (I.P.P.) and goals may be formulated. You will see these plans placed chronologically through the book interspersed with Don's poems.

The reports are of two types: the professional evaluation done by the staff (the I.P.P.), and the daily comments, feelings, and personal reflections of the staff concerning Bethy, her family, and other influences on her life. We thought those who work professionally with children would be interested in following her technical progress.

What does the future hold for our Bethany? No one knows for certain. But we believe in her and in other children like her. Bethany will make it. Our hope is that those she meets now will do what her family has always done—and it's so easy—just love her and give her time.

Lee Ann Britain, Director
Infant Development Center
Shawnee Mission Medical Center

Introduction

Our family has had twice as many retarded children as almost any other family around. We had two: "Bethy"—Bethany Flagg Bakely, our seventh child, was born June 14, 1976, and still hangs around the house. The "Mouse"—Matthew David Bakely, our fifth child, was born March 10, 1960, and died September 7, 1965. This book is about them.

It's more about Bethy simply because I started writing about her on the night she was born, and I keep a running commentary on her as I watch her grow. It's less about the "Mouse" because I had only written a few things about him while he lived, and because I no longer have the luxury of watching his growth, pain, moods, and joys each day. In the years since his death, of course, I've lost so much of him from my mind. So, a small bit of him (whatever I could dredge up from my memory, the memories of my wife, Jeanne, our other children, and folks who knew him) is included in this book.

The difference between Matthew and Bethy, in some ways, is astronomical. Matthew was microcephalic (he was born with an abnormally small brain). Jeanne had food poisoning during her second month of pregnancy with him. We had gotten some bad chicken while we were camping and it made us all severely ill. We have never known for sure that the sickness was a major contributor in Matthew's condition, but it surely seemed like a logical culprit. At any rate, Matthew was born with a portion of his brain either missing or, at least seriously underdeveloped.

His condition was obvious at birth. He required constant care. He could never sit up by himself, walk, talk, chew, or purposely hold anything in his hand. Yet, he wasn't just mush. He was an exciting, wonderful, loving person inside that non-working body. He suffered much pain, and was sick—often to the edge of death. He was great agony to us, but he was greater joy.

In the 1960s, there wasn't much help for him.

Professionals knew little about his condition and were cautious about using their time on a person with a condition that they knew so little about. I searched through university and professional libraries in an effort to learn as much as I could about this condition and potential, but all I could find were a few fairly useless, non-encouraging paragraphs.

As a family, we surrounded him with love. We spent hour after hour searching for those things which would give him the faintest glimmer of progress. We exercised him, played, talked, explained, and worked with him for his whole lifetime. In fact, it took two years of working with him every day to teach him to say the simple sound, "O."

But when he did it—when he finally did it—we knew at that moment that he wanted to get out of that prison of his as badly as we wanted to get him out! We were so thrilled! Two years, every day, and it finally paid off!

The professionals had told us that he could never do this. They said that he couldn't possibly control the effort and the mechanics which would allow him to produce a speaking sound. But he did.

When we took him back to the professionals to show them what he could do, they asked us how long it took us to teach him that little trick—and told us to come back when he had conquered "m" or "p." We didn't go back to them anymore. It just seemed that it was going to be harder to teach them, than it was to teach him.

We started working with him on the sound "l," but he died before we got him that far.

Paul, our eldest, was fourteen when the "Mouse" died. Lois, the youngest, was two, three years younger than the "Mouse." They were all children then, but they were proud of their brother, and very involved in his progress. Their pride was very contagious, and their feelings about him rubbed off on all who met them.

"Mouse" (we called him that because he was so small) died when he was five, three months after we moved from New Jersey to Kansas. He didn't know what life was like without love. That's a pretty neat deal. Few people get to experience life that way.

Bethy is a totally different case. In fact, she's much more like the other kids in our family than she is like Matthew. If we ranged them on a scale of similarities, with Matthew as a 1 and the other kids as 10s, Bethy would be closer to an 8 or 9.

Jeanne and I were in our late forties when Bethy was born. The first six had come in the space of twelve years. The youngest was thirteen when Bethy was born. As you can imagine, Bethy was known, around our house, as the "shock of our lives."

Bethy's condition was not as obvious as Matthew's at her birth. We knew, of course, that there was a strong chance, because of our ages, that she'd be born with Down's syndrome, so it didn't come as a total shock to us. And having had the "Mouse," the possibility of her being retarded wasn't a revolting or terribly fearful thought to us.

Because of some problems, Bethy was born by Caesarian Section. They let me in the operating room, next to Jeanne, while it happened. I tried to avoid watching them make the initial cuts because I didn't want to see them cut this special woman and because, as this was a new experience for me, I wasn't sure how I'd react. You see, I'm an exparatrooper, did a lot of fighting, was in trouble with the law, and was kicked out of home and school when I was seventeen. I am about six feet tall and weigh 200 pounds. The idea of sliding to the floor in a dead faint while they cut her was totally unappealing to me.

But Linda, a nurse friend of ours, was with us during the operation. As they started to cut, she called me to come watch, and I couldn't very well refuse. So I watched.

It was fantastic! A miracle! They cut through

the layers, and when they got to the baby, a nurse pulled out just her legs, spread them like a wishbone, and shouted to me, "It's a girl." (I had hoped for a more delicate first view of my daughter!)

After they cleaned her up, they immediately handed her to me. This squishy little thing was ours! And I loved her—right then.

After a moment of introducing her to the fine art of snuggling and hugging, I held her out to get a good look at her. And there were the signs. Those "Downsy" eyes, the bent pinky fingers, the lifeline all the way across the hand.

I asked the doctor if she had Down's. He wasn't sure, so he and Linda took her away and in twenty minutes came back with the report, "She has Down's."

Dr. Ken and Linda were good friends, so they were feeling dejected for us. But I had already had twenty minutes to think about it, so when they made the announcement, I was already feeling better about it than they were. After all, they had never had the wonderful experience of Matthew.

She was our daughter and I felt that God had ways of turning all this into a blessing. After I was reasonably sure that the information was correct, I decided that it was time to tell the rest of the family. They had gathered at our house and were waiting to hear about the baby. I didn't want to telephone because I felt that if they took it hard, it was important for me to be with them. Anyway, Jeanne was still unconscious, so I decided that I could go home for a little while to be with them.

When I got there, I told them that they had a sister, Bethany Flagg Bakely (her mother's maiden name was Flagg), told them her weight, that Mom was OK, and that Beth had Down's syndrome.

There was silence for a minute. Lois, thirteen, was only two when Matthew had died, and hadn't had the chance to experience him very much. She began to cry quietly. Then one of the others spoke, "Hey—we can handle *that!*" And I thought, "Bethany Flagg Bakely, you have come to the right house!" And she had!

The older children had already begun to scatter from our home, so Lois, who was the only one still at home, became a second mother to Beth—a friend, mother, sister, playmate—so loving, so proud of her little sister.

Let me quickly introduce the rest of our children.

Paul was born in 1951. At the moment of this writing, he is working for Cross-Lines (the inner-city church agency of which I am executive director). He left college to marry and is now going back to finish his degree.

Steve, born in 1953, was a music major until Bethy was born, then changed to music therapy. He just finished his internship in a state mental hospital in Texas, and is working at a group home for mentally handicapped adults in the Kansas City area.

Claudia, born in 1955, is a graduate nurse, married, and has been working with birth-disabled babies in the infant intensive care unit at the Kansas University Medical Center.

Pete, born in 1958, is an actor with the Missouri Repertory Theater, and is working on his acting degree at the University of Missouri.

Lois, born in 1963, just graduated from high school, made her first parachute jump, and is majoring in art therapy at Emporia State College in Emporia, Kansas.

They all were in the National Honor Society and are all working, or have worked, their own way through college. Each one's adventures would fill a book.

They are all wonderful with Bethy. Naturally, this is all a great source of comfort for Jeanne and myself. We know that we aren't alone in rearing Bethy, and we know that with brothers and sisters like Bethy's, we don't have to fear for her future.

The rest of our relatives and friends have been wonderful. Many of them remembered

Matthew, and remembered what he had meant to them, and remembered how much he meant to, and did for, us. They had watched us all through Matthew's life, and they knew, from our history, that Bethy would not be a crushing blow to us. They already knew that remarks such as, "Oh, you poor things," and "We're so sorry," were inappropriate. They didn't have to go through that whole awkward thing of "What do we say? How do we handle this?" They were able to read our joy and commitment from the start, and so were at ease with us and with Bethy.

My father, who never got his rough edges sanded down, sent us a note when he heard of Bethy's birth and of her Down's syndrome. It said, "Just think, Bud [his name for me], some families never even get to have one retarded child. You and Jeanne were lucky enough to get two."

He was right. And the reason he knew we'd feel that way was that somewhere along the line he and my mother had set the tone that helped us to see Bethy and the "Mouse" as joy, and as special gifts in slightly different packages.

Not only is Bethy much different from Matthew, conditions surrounding the retarded are different today than they were when Matthew was alive. As recently as the '40s, Down's children were hustled off to state institutions, often to vegetate. Their life span was predicted to be about fifteen years. They were thought of and referred to as "Mongolian idiots."

Things are very different now. Early intervention is common. For example, Bethy started school at the Infant Development Center (now connected with the Shawnee Mission Medical Center in Johnson County, Kansas) when she was one month old. For the first five years of her life, she went several half-days per week. At first, they worked on muscle development and physical progress. Instead of having the traditional chubby little mushy-muscled body, she's very sturdy, strong, healthy—but short. They

didn't seem to be able to do anything about 'tall.' She still has some problems with balance and coordination. She seems to conquer each problem just a little later than other children, but eventually, she does conquer them. She's normal in most things. Where her condition does hold her back, she catches up. Her speech, comprehension, and social skills are fairly close to normal.

Starting public school this fall, in regular classes, with no special education, will be an experiment for the school system as well as for her and us. But things have changed. As a society we have learned much about kids like her. We must get ready for them. There are lots of Bethys coming along, and with our help, they can be useful, producing citizens. We need to make up our minds that there will be no more scrap heaps made up of people like her.

Of course, we, as a family, are nervous about her going to "regular" school. The schools are, too. Bethy will be a first for them. How will the teachers handle her? Will she be looked at as another problem? How will the other kids treat her? Wrong attitudes can hurt her a lot, can cause a very important experiment to fail, and can hurt thousands who follow her.

We and the school are both open to change. If we find that we are pushing her too far and too fast, we will adapt. If we find that she needs special education classes, of course we will shift that way.

Our hopes for her are that she will acquire and develop the kinds of skills and attitudes that she will need to live life at its fullest. We also hope that she will be able to live independently, that she will find some special skill or gift which will be unique to her, and that she will see herself as a giver—a contributor—not just a receiver. We hope to help her find the faith, personality, and strength to be able to deal with the confusions of life, and to be as victorious as possible over the temptation to feel badly about herself. Of course, these are the things we want for our other kids as well. We even harbor hopes that Bethy will eventually graduate from high school. We realize that this is more and more a possibility.

The chances of our living to see her get through her twenties are getting slimmer and slimmer. After all, we are both in our fifties now. For kids like her, the twenties are usually pretty formative years. Job skills, independent living training, etc., are usually still a large part of their lives during those years. So, seeing her "settled" is probably a luxury that we won't have. As I said before, we're not too worried about that. Her brothers and sisters will be around when we're not. And so will lots of others who care.

Many agencies, institutions, and individuals are studying and learning about mentally handicapped persons. Doors are being opened on their behalf. Another encouraging note is that so many of the people who are working with handicapped persons today are doing it out of a sense of commitment. They seem excited about what these persons are learning and accomplishing. Very few of the people who are looking to specialize in working with the retarded seem to be just "looking for a job." We have been impressed with the faculty, students, and staffs of many of the schools which prepare students to work with retarded persons.

The church, too, is seeing this work as a part of its ministry. I speak several hundred times a year around the country. It always thrills me when I go to churches like the First United Methodist in Lawrence, Kansas, or the First Christian Church in Beloit, Kansas, where I see many retarded persons taking an active and natural part in the worship and programs of the church. Valley View and Bristol Hill United Methodist churches in the Kansas City area have special programs and services for the retarded persons and families in their areas, as lots of other churches do.

Businesses are adapting to the handicapped

in various ways. Job training, independent and semi-independent living situations, research facilities, and a myriad of services for the retarded and their families have made this a much better world for the retarded and for all of us. And, of course, places like the Infant Development Center, where speech, music, art, occupational, physical, and many other kinds of therapies are mixed with love and skills in such a way as to help handicapped persons become joyful and useful persons.

Many people are breaking the molds and changing many minds about the handicapped persons. Look, if you are going to have a retarded child, this is as good a time as any. So, go right ahead. Two hundred years ago was a rotten time. Fifty years ago, folks were stashing retarded people away in institutions. Twenty-five years ago many were being hidden away in their homes, and families were ashamed to admit that their child was retarded.

But, today it's changing. We are learning how to turn agonies into triumphs, and we are all better for it. Today I see parents, families, communities, and helpers with intense pride in the achievements of their retarded friends. If you want to see this attitude at work, go to the next Special Olympics competition that you hear about. It may just be the most fun-filled, exciting, encouraging day of your life.

Finally, a word to—and about—other parents of retarded children. I must confess that when I am with other parents of retarded children—and especially when I am asked to speak to groups of parents—I get nervous. There are so many different feelings and approaches to deal with. Some feel cursed. Some are overwhelmed with the changes that these children make in their lives. Some are touchy about feelings which disagree with theirs.

I listen to some and I wonder if that's the way I'm really supposed to feel. I ask myself if other parents see me as slightly out of touch with reality and with present-day knowledge. I also wonder if my expressed feelings cause them pain.

Sometimes when I listen to other parents, I try to reevaluate some of the things I think about Bethy and the "Mouse" and I wonder if I am just psyching myself into all these positive thoughts. Maybe I am. I guess we all have our ways of coping. We parents seem to need some kind of response that works for us.

As for me, I've often said that when God invented Down's syndrome, it was one of God's best days. What God wanted for us was the closest expression of pure, unadulterated love since Jesus. I think that if I had to choose a child to raise, at my age, I'd choose Down's syndrome. The kid brings me more happiness and joy than a roomful of somebody else's puppies.

Now and then people say, "Of course, you feel that way about Bethy. She's healthy, bright, in regular classes in regular school. You've hardly got a retarded kid at all."

I hear that and agree. Bethy is easy to take. But do remember that the "Mouse" was also our child and that we were thankful to have him, too. We felt enriched and blessed by his life.

There are lots of Bethanys and Matthews in this world. We need them. They seem to bring out such good things in us, once we get to know them. They give us a special quality in our lives. They draw us out of our selfishness. They inspire us. They give us much more than they take. This world would lose so much without them.

To the many like Bethy and the "Mouse," and to those who care for them, I'm glad you happened to us. I thank God for his wisdom in sending you our way.

The word retarded

I am not unaware of the problems surrounding the use of the word "retarded." Having spoken to many folks about it, I find no clear consensus on the proper word to use. I do, however, find clear opinions. Some folks are absolutely insistent that the proper term is "developmentally disabled." Others insist that the only term is "mentally handicapped."

Frankly, I just don't know which term is correct—or least offensive. I find great disagreement and often intense feelings surrounding the many different terms, and those feelings are spread out among parents, clients, professionals, and other interested persons.

I recognize that we are, at this point, in a transitional stage regarding our terms. Not being much of a prophet, I don't know which word or phrase is eventually going to win. Frankly, when Bethy is old enough to think about the terms and to deal with them, I think she is going to be equally offended by being labeled "mentally handicapped" or "developmentally disabled" as by being labeled "retarded."

All I can say is that I'm in a quandry about the proper term. I use several in this book— whichever felt right at the time.

I'm not writing the book as a professional in the field. I'm writing it as a father—a father who desperately loves his little girl and who still loves his son, even though the "Mouse" has been dead for almost twenty years.

Donald C. Bakely

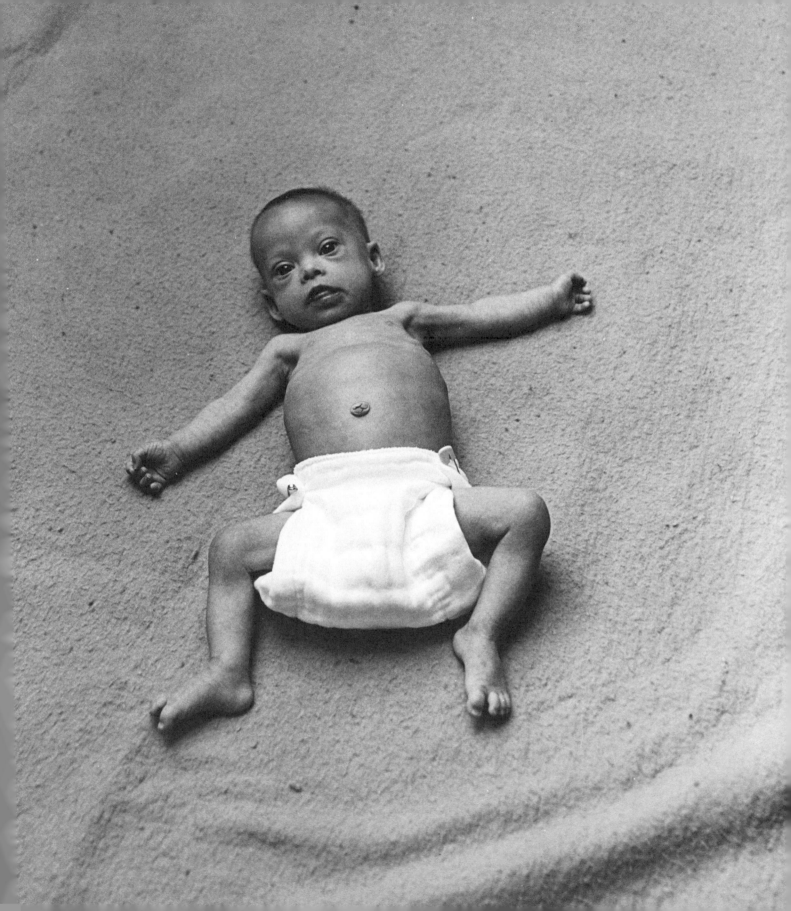

We keep looking for gifts
                    in regular packages.
If I wrapped one
                in newspaper
                or in a brown paper bag
            or if it was something
                            I found in a field
                            instead of the shelf of a store,
it wouldn't seem
                as *legitimate*
                    a gift.

If it cost me
            feeling
        instead of
            money,
        it would seem
                    somehow
                        not as worthy.
Maybe that's because
        we can't transfer
            our feelings
                to others
                    as easily
                        as money.

Well—
        Beth
            is one of those special gifts of God
                            in different wrapping.
        She's a gift
            from
                God's
                    feelings.

Maybe the hardest thing
    about receiving a gift in special packaging
        isn't
            understanding the gift
            or understanding
                that it *is* a gift—
Maybe the problem is
    that we don't know how
        to explain the gift
            and the feeling behind it
  to those
    who only look
        for regular packages.

(November, 1975)

You say
    funny things have been happening
                to your period lately?
Well,
    we *are* getting the right age
            for menopause—
    a *little* young,
        but sometimes it happens at our age.
And menopause
    is at least better than that *other* possibility—.

Still—
        have it checked out.
We wouldn't want it to be a problem
                  that was dangerous to you.

(December, 1975)

                        I

Pregnant!!!
        Pregnant!!!
You think you are pregnant???

Not *now*!
        Not at *our* age!!
Our kids are almost grown—.
We were just talking about your finally being able
        to travel with me,
                sharing the things
                    I only get to see
                        by myself.

Pregnant??
        Aw-------it *couldn't* be.
I don't even remember being
                  careless
                    in our love—do you?

II

Lord,

    Let me explain something to you.

        Are you listening?

        Are you paying *any* attention?

           I'd like this to be clear to you!

Hear this—

    If you'd really like to know,

             we'd rather not!!!

    If there's a chance,

        any chance,

           that she's not pregnant,

I'd appreciate it

        if

        you'd tip the scales that way!

Not now. Not again.

Who needs to have raised one large family

        and *then* one only child?

Who needs 45 years of P.T.A.?

Who needs to look forward

        to another kid

          becoming a teenager?

    (When this one's 13, I'll be 61!)

You are known for your kindness.

    How about spilling a little on us now—

        in our hour of need?

Look,

    if you can't arrange kindness,

        I'll take some simple *justice*.

III

Yet, Lord,

    whatever—

of course we yield to your wisdom.

You've been in business
a long time
and have always impressed me
with your wisdom—
even when you have interfered
with my life.
And when we have disagreed in the past
you always seem to outsmart me
and your way
turned out right
and best.
So whatever happens,
we accept.
And we will accept with joy
and trust.

Even though we'd rather not go through this,
we will
—if it happens—
and we'll pull out all the stops,
and do our best,
and love it well,
and make it warm
and things will be OK.

You know that we'll be ready, Lord.
It's just that it's kind of a shock.
But we'll get over the shock
—if it's true—.
I just wanted you to know
that
we'd rather
not!

(Written the Night of Her Birth)

I

My baby?
My brand new Beth?
Down's syndrome???

Why, God?
What in the world is the matter with you?
What is there
      that gives you jollies
                in creating
                      partial people?
Why?
Did you think things were getting
                too easy
                    for us?
Damn!!!
      Why??
Anyway,
      why *us*?
Haven't you noticed,
         we've *paid* our dues!

Matthew—
    microcephalic
    never able to sit up
        hold up his head
        walk
        talk
        chew
        hold anything in his hand
    every sickness slamming him to the edge of dying.

Mom-Mom—
    arteriosclerosis
    colitis
    argumentative

confused
pesty
dependent.

Why Beth too?
Why do you want us to spend
                    the rest of our years
                            explaining
                            training
                            sheltering
                            carrying
                                    our last child?
I'm tired tonight, God
        and I'm too dammed
                            old
                            for this.
We wanted to be free
                    to travel
                    to be without kids
                    to enjoy some years
                            by ourselves.

But you did it to us again,
                    didn't you?
Why??
Why *us*??
We don't deserve this!

                            II
Hey—
        I've been thinking, Lord.
Let me rephrase that.

Why *not* us?
We've certainly had
                plenty of practice.

And, Lord,
    when we get over these first few moments,
        you know we've got
            the feeling
             for it.
And come to think of it,
    we've got a family that will love her.
    We can certainly
        surround her with joy.
And that's what you need for her,
            isn't it?

Hey—
    Matthew did us good,
        not evil.
    He and Mom-Mom made us grow,
            be patient
            stretch our love,
            learn about caring,
            and teach others.
      And that's
        the good stuff
        of life.

    They helped us touch other lives
            in a caring kind of way.
Lord,
    thanks for reminding me.
We *are* right for this child.
And,
    after all,
        we *are* your children
           committed
            to your will.
And,
    if this is your will,
      it must be good
        for all of us.

We *will* do
        what you ask.
And if you think
        our shared lives
      can do good for each other,
            that's OK with us.

                III
Yeah—why not?
        Why *not* us?
Hey—
     I saw her birth—
        saw them cut my wife
           and wrench this child
                into life.
        They let me hold her right away
           and feel her cheeks on mine.
     I watched her tiny hands and feet quiver.
     Saw her as she struggled
           to squeeze open
               her eyes.

And I love her, Lord,
        already.
I don't care if she's got
        webbed feet.
    She's mine.
    And we need
        each other.

I'm still asking,
        why, Lord?
But the question is changed for me.
Why, Lord?
        Why did you choose to bless us again?

Why,
    out of all the possible families
        did you choose us
            for this
                armful
                    of love?
I was right before.
    We don't deserve this.
        But
            you have a way
                of blessing us
                    past
                        our deserving.

If you had given us the choice,
    we would have said no.
    and we would have missed
                these special moments
                    of giving and receiving
                    and growing
                        in love.

Thank you, Lord,
    for being smarter
            than we are.

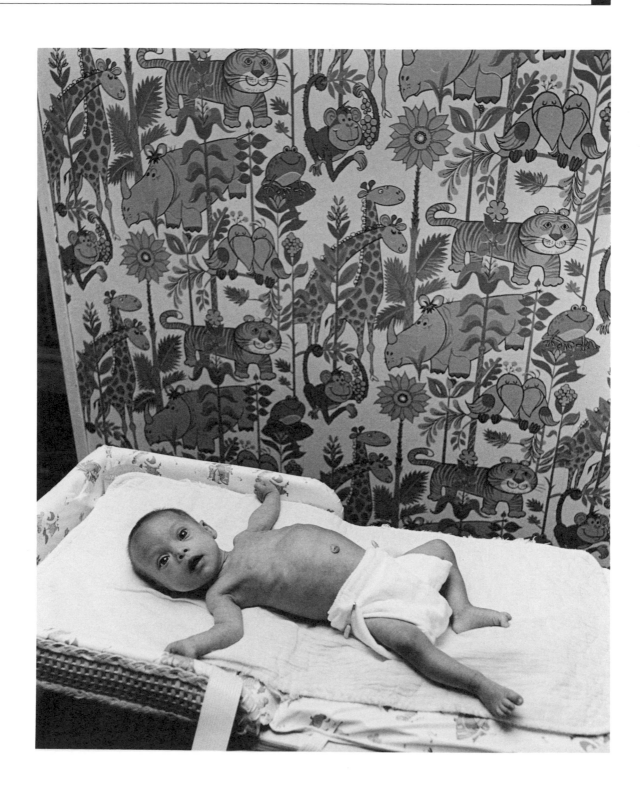

"Don't worry about tomorrow.
        It'll have enough worries of its own."
Jesus
        keeps making sense to me.
It's Beth's tomorrows
                that cause us pain.
            Who will she be?
            What care will she need?
            How much pain will others give her?
            Will life be embarrassing for her
                        —or us?
            What will happen to her—tomorrow?
            What will happen when *we* die—
            Who will love her—tomorrow?

A lot of todays,
        coming clumped up,
            still in the dark
                are called *tomorrows*—
                        and they have worries
                            tacked on.

Her tomorrows
            are frightening.

But if we do
        what Jesus advises,
            (take no thought of tomorrow)
        and just take her each day,
                    it's different.

Because *today*
            she's warm
                and soft to my touch.
        She excites
            and delights us.
        We watch her hands move gently.
        Her eyes

squinch
in response to love.
She snuggles in the morning
and gently stretches her arms
to feel us both
beside her.
Her cries are for
this moment's
pains,
not for
tomorrow's
fears.
We watch her try out
a new face
or sound,
response,
or move;
and today
is a day
full
of the joy
of our baby.

It's only her
tomorrows
that frighten me.
The todays
bring us joy
and make us anxious
to touch her face.

The todays
are
God's gift to us.
The tomorrows
belong to God.

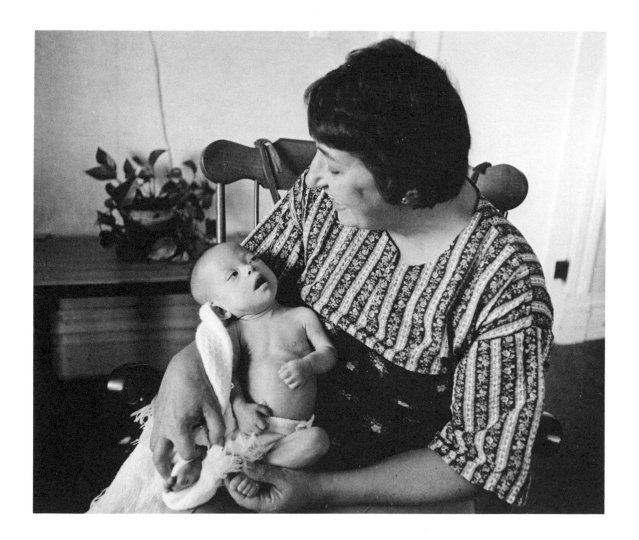

Isn't it a special wisdom
that God
gently slips the tomorrows to us
one day at a time
and turns them from
a clump
of fears
into joys and pains
that
we can handle?

INFANT DEVELOPMENT CENTER

Bethany Bakely-1. INDIVIDUAL PROGRAM PLAN—STAFF EVALUATION

4 Weeks - (Excerpt from Physical Therapist's report)

Assessment - A 1-month-old Down's child functioning at approximately the 1 month level in motor skills. She is an alert baby who interacts well with her environment through both her vision and hearing, although she prefers her hearing. She keeps herself content with hand-to-mouth activities and sucking on her fingers. If this does not work she enjoys being hugged and cuddled and snuggles nicely into the arms.

Therapy Plan - Mother and child will meet with Mothers of the Down's syndrome group, and their children, for ½ hour and then both Mother and child will be involved in a 1½ hour stimulation session.
Mother was instructed today to:
1. Place the child on her stomach.
2. Use hearing and visual stimulation together and then decrease hearing stimulation to increase visual focusing and tracking.
3. Place the child over a small roll to encourage head lifting via both visual and hearing stimulation and support on forearms.

2. STAFF COMMENTS   1 thru 7 months

Beth - Progress Notes

7-16-76   Beth worked hard at bringing her head up when over the roll. The vibrator seemed to facilitate this. In visual focusing and tracking she did best when the colored balls were paired with the bell. "It's hard, but we're doing better."

9-14-76   Parents indicated no true progress had been made.

10-26-76   Concern re: size and failure to grow.

11-16-76   Mom reports Beth has gained two ounces.

1-3-77   Feeding in supported sitting in high chair. Beth alert and happy today.

2-1-77   Reaching and grasping in supine. Vocalizing more. Bearing more weight on lower extremities. Sitting more erect.

(One Month)

Touching her brings joy
                    and gratitude.

One day
        her face was close,
                her eyes were alive with the happies,
                        her body was pressing me with the snugglies,
                                and her loving was warming my moments.

And inside,
        my whole being
                said, "Thanks, Lord!
                        Thanks for this soft,
                                warm,
                                        loving blessing!"

And inside,
        immediately,
                I felt response.
        "I thought you'd like this one, Don.
        Isn't she just something *special*?"

Reaffirmation—
            Beth is another
                        special
                                gift in our lives.

You didn't get much of a nose, Kid.

It looks like somebody
            dropped
                    the end of a red jelly bean
                            on your face.
But you *did* get big eyes, Kid.
        Big,
            talkative,
                commandeering,
                        intense blue (like your Dad!)
                                eyes.
And that mouth—
        strong,
            sweet,
                sloppy,
                    drippy,
                        turn-me-inside-out-with-a-smile,
                                mouth.
And a face
        just jam packed
                with *you*.
You've got Down's, all right.
No question about it.
But right now,
            I couldn't care less
                    if you had three legs, Kid.
'Cause you're just right for
                huggin'
                kissin'
                lovin'
                watchin'
                and thankin' God for.
It's a *great* face, Kid.
And it does
        so many
            neat
                things.

It's special—
like
the rest of you.

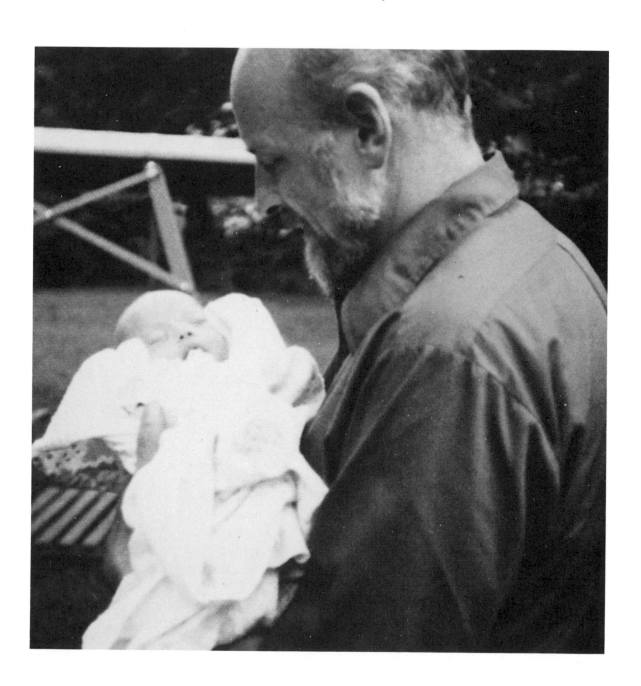

I think I understand
　　　　　why you
　　　　　　　happened
　　　　　　　　to us, Kid,
But I'm not sure I understand
　　　　　　　why this
　　　　　　　　happened
　　　　　　　　　to you!
　　　Why some tiny chromosome
　　　　　　　　　decided to go astray
　　and why it decided to do it
　　　　　　　　in *your* body.
If I have trouble understanding it,
　　　　　　so,
　　　　　　　of course,
　　　　　　　　will you.

Yet the time will come
　　　　　　when you will understand *this*
　　that something serious,
　　　　　　　lasting,
　　　　　　　　and uncorrectable,
　　has completely
　　　　　　affected your life.

What if,
　　　　when those moments come to you,
　　　　　you aren't as able to accept
　　　　　　　　that
　　　as we are able,
　　　　　happy,
　　　　　honored,
　　　　　tickled,
　　　　　　to accept
　　　　　　　you?

Is there a way, Child?
Is there a way, Jeanne?
Is there a way, Experts?
Is there a way, Lord,
            that we can keep her pleased
                                with who she is
                    rather than depressed
                                about who she is not?
We have the feeling
            that it was a special wisdom,
                    and not a special curse,
            that made her
                    for this world
            and put her in our hands.
And we suspect
            that there is also
                    a special grace
                            given to us
                                    in the whole package
                    —a grace to correspond
                            to her needs.
The time is coming
            when we may need
                    to cash some of that in.

Give us that measure
                    of wisdom
                    and love
            that can surround her
                with the kind of acceptance
                            that can't easily
                                be cracked
                when she begins to ask
                    why
                            this all
                                happened
                                    to her.

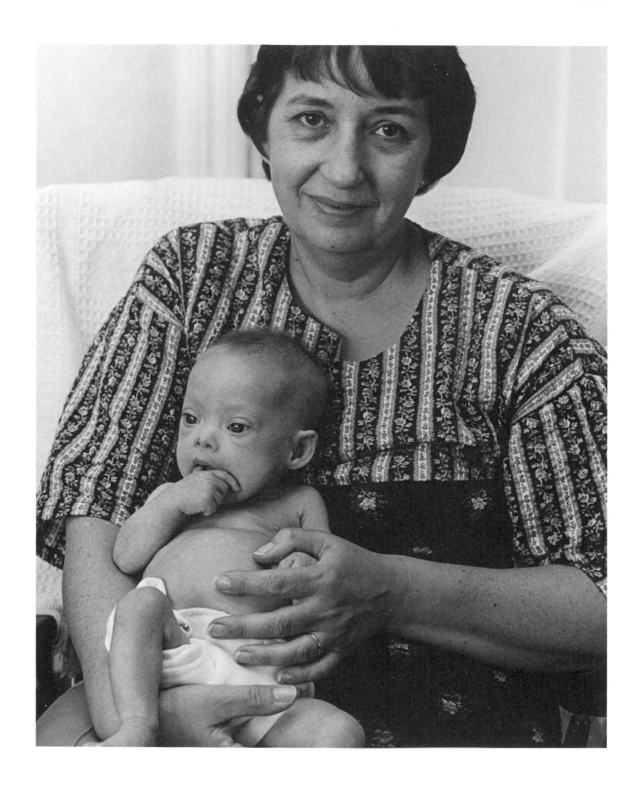

"Don't let the world squeeze you into its mold."
I didn't think
          you knew Scripture, Kid.
But you surely do practice
              that verse.

You are the loviest—most hardheaded,
          sweetest—most obstinate
                    bundle of baby
                          I ever met.
They say it comes with your condition, Kid,
      and I guess we are going to have to learn
                    to live with it,
               and even learn
                  to like it.
How can somebody your size
              insist
          so hard?

You can't talk,
        but
            you surely can communicate
                  and let your "no's"
                      be known.
Your cantankerousness
              is sometimes hard for us to live with,
      but somehow I know
              it's going to serve you well
      as you learn to live in,
            with,
           and sometimes against your world,
      as that world tries to squeeze you
                into its mold,

and as you, in turn,
    tell that world
        just what you'll accept,
        what you are comfortable with,
        and how much you are willing
          to stand.
I'm torn between teaching you to adapt to your world's ways
    and not wanting to stifle that special gift,
        that special personality
          that is uniquely you.

The world has much to learn
    from the special
      loving,
      "don't-push-me,"
        person
         that you are.
Your insistent ways
    may be
      your best defense in life,
  and I'm glad
    (I think)
      that you have them.

(Five Months)

You're so new!

Yet,
        you've already learned so much.
You know how to use your body,
                                eyes,
                                mouth,
                                        to give me messages.
You seem to feel some satisfaction
                                        in the way
                                                you've trained me.
(I thought I was supposed to be training *you*!)
You lie in the playpen,
                        growing weary of the same
                                        sights and sounds.
I keep making the same two mistakes—
        I seem to always pass by at the wrong moment
        and I let our eyes meet.
Immediately
        your eyes flash
                        that Hi-I'm-adorable-and-cuddly,
                                        wouldn't-you-like-to-hold-me look.
You have a split second to tell
                        if that did the job.
You compute its effectiveness,
        sense me passing by,
        and the bottom lip (fastest bottom lip in the west),
                jumps right out.

It suckers me
                into watching
                                for that fatal one more second

while the body stiffens,
      the belly arches up
      and the face insists,
            begs,
            charms,
            woos,
            loves,
            shouts
                  pick me up!
And I'm hooked again,
            trapped by a seven-pound brute of insistence.
Yeah.
      Your infancy training process
                  is going well, Kid.
And
      I know
            who's getting trained!

(Six Months)

When I hold you,
                  tiny woman,
When I hold you,
            the world becomes
                        a warmer place.
How did you learn
                  such love
                        in six
                              short
                                    months?
The special moments
            when I sit back in my chair
            and you lie on my chest

first
        looking in my eyes
then
        making long senseless noises
                        and sentences
            that somehow say
                        a lot of special things to me,
are moments
        that glue us, Kid.

(I think I'm glad
            that you can't talk yet,
    because—for a while—
        I can put loving feelings
                    behind
                    what I can assume to be
                        your
                            loving sounds.)
Then,
    after we've said
                enough good things
                    to each other,
    the moment comes
                when you tell me the best of all
                            without words.
One long,
        loving look,
            straight at me,
                eyeball to eyeball—
    lasting 'til you are sure it's said
                and received.
Then the head
        lies on my chest
                and we belong,
                    really belong!
And I know the love is there.

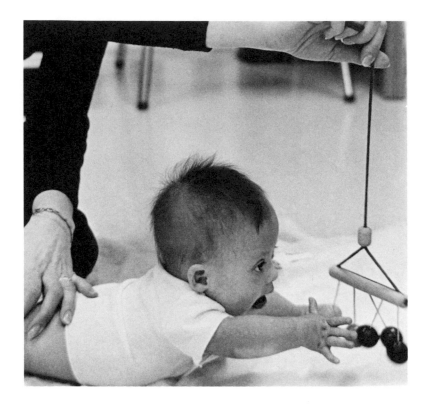

The trust,
the comfort,
the way you melt
        into my body
      says we are *friends*
          and we both know it.
You
    melt good,
        Kid.
And it
    seals
       us.
And
    I
    need
       that!

INFANT DEVELOPMENT CENTER

1. INDIVIDUAL PROGRAM PLAN — STAFF EVALUATION

7 Months - Physical Therapist describes Beth as alert and sociable. At this time she:
   1. Lifts her head when placed on her stomach.
   2. Reaches for toys and faces.
   3. Quiets to sounds.
   4. Laughs and vocalizes.
   5. Shows decreased muscle tone and muscle strength.

Assessment: Beth is a 7-month-old Down's, functioning as follows:

Language	5 Months
Cognition (Education/Thinking/Reasoning)	5-6 Months
Fine motor and perceptual motor (use of hands)	4 Months
Gross Motor (Large motor skills)	4½ Months
Self Help, feeding	6 Months
Social	5 Months

In the past 6 months, Beth has made 4-6 months progress.

Long Term Goal: Placement in preschool when age appropriate.

Short Term Goals: 1. Improve head control and sitting balance.
   2. Improve muscle tone and strength.
   3. Facilitate reach and grasp.
   4. Facilitate better rolling.

2. STAFF COMMENTS   7 to 14 months

2-1-77   Reaching and grasping in supine. Vocalizing more. Bearing more weight on lower extremities. Sitting more erect.

3-1-77   Tolerated supporting on hands in prone over roll.

3-15-77   Marked improvement in past week.

3-22-77   Fussy today — not too cooperative.

3-29-77   Sat alone for 40 seconds!

4-5-77   Using right more than left with reaching. Work on two-handed activities.

5-17-77   Remains in 4-point position if placed for short period of time if lower extremities are stabilized. Standing with hyperextension of knees. Physical assist needed to support self in sitting with hands out to either side. Tilting reactions in prone and supine improved. Protective extension in sitting with some assist.

5-24-77   Beth anticipates object around head in both directions. Protective reactions elicited with assist. Pivots 45 degrees in both directions. Moves a few inches forward to obtain object with some assist. Tilting reactions elicited to right and left in sitting. Send home therapy program for summer.

(January 18—Evaluation Day at the Infancy Training Center)

Big day, Kid!
Big,
     good
          day.
Evaluation day for you
     by the people
          who have been teaching you
               so much.
Carolyn checks you out,
     questions us,
     tests you.

Social skills — near seven months,
Motor skills — around five months.
          Much progress, thanks to them!

You seem to try so hard
     and
          you make us *so* proud.
Think of it!
          a baby who *tries*!
Most babies just get to grow.
You have to *strain*!
And
     you do it.

Then
     to the doctor.
And today,
     finally,
          you are past ten pounds!

You,
    the skinny baby
        who hardly gained
            for months,
        who looked like an ad
            for world hunger.
There's meat on you, Kid—
        even some fat.
And you
    finally
      feel sturdy
        and strong,
        and out of the woods!

We *are* going to make it, Kid.
And you *are* going to stay
        to grow
        and learn
        and teach
        and love
        and share your life
           with us.
It's been a good day, Kid,
    and we jumped a lot of hurdles
        together.

(One Year)

They fit,
    so I guess you think
            babies' thumbs
            and thumbnails
        are *supposed* to go up daddies' noses
               while daddies are asleep!

I must admit
    if I were your size
        and there was a still, sleeping face
               near my lap
    I'd think it was a lovely place
           to test two jaggedy,
            razor-edged,
           brand new
              teeth.

After all,
    how are you to know
        that a single shove
           of one sharp finger
        or the clawing act
           of a tiny hand
isn't the way to move the eyelid
    so you can see that shiny marble
        that you know
           is behind that little flap of skin?
And yes,
    the beard is not supposed
              to rip off.
  No—
    not in large clumps
    or in strands of two or three
           still attached to my mustache.

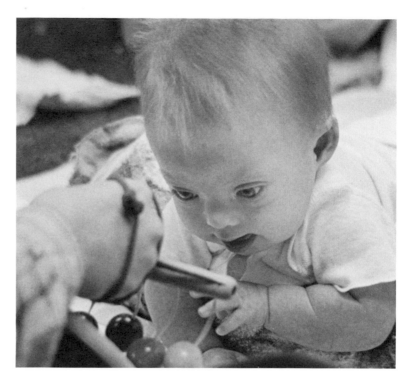

A double-handed whack
            on my bald head
      followed by
            a pint of slobber
                        intended as a kiss
      and offset by looks of sheer passion
                  and absolute innocence
            tells me that all this
                        says
                        love and trust.

Kid,
      pain for pain's sake hurts.
But the pain that I can stand
      is the pain that comes
                  from a pair
                        of your lovin' hands.

As I drive across Kansas
                    in the different moments of the year
        I'm thankful for the many ways
                    beauty
                            makes itself known,
        and even more thankful that
                    somewhere
                    somehow I was taught
            that beauty can be found
                            in lots of likely
                                and unlikely
                                    places.
I love the sharp silhouette
                of a once-live tree
        in those moments when the morning pushes its light out
            to prepare the way for the day.
I find
        the desolation of eastern Utah
                            moving
                            inspiring,
                            breathtaking.
The beige, cattle-specked hills of Kansas
        always touch me
                    with the warmth
                            of their beauty.
And yet,
        others have spoken to me in despair
                of the emptiness
                    the boring-ness
                        of these same things.

I think this happens also with Down's people.

I remember seeing Down's kids before,
            and thinking the word
                    "homely."

But that was before you, Beth
and you, Stacey,
and you, Jennifer,
and the rest of Beth's schoolmates
who, since Beth,
have infected
my life.
When I see those sweet gushing mouths,
those almost left-out noses,
those eyes that are always getting ready
to do something,
and the rest
of what you come with,
then I am reminded that God,
the ultimate artist,
has a better sense of beauty
than we have.
And in you,
God gave us a beauty
that runs amok
and that moves
all up and down
and in and around
our senses.
The special thing
for those of us who have Down's kids,
is that God gave us a beauty
that can be hugged.
And when it's hugged,
it somehow
becomes enlarged
and special
in its power
to move.
Beauty was meant to be sensed
and yours is a beauty
that touches
me.

(One Year)

You're a sneaky little kid, aren't you?
With all our efforts
                    to teach you differently,
        the dog knows she can count on you
                    to get the food to her
                                that you don't like
                            (or *do* like, for that matter).
So at mealtimes,
        she sits patiently at the foot of your high chair
                waiting—
        and
                as surely as night follows day,
                    that little hand
                                whips the food to the floor.

Even if you like it all,
        she knows that her soft whine
                will be a signal for you to share.

Sometimes you check our eyes for a "no,"
        and while watching us
                and seeing the "no,"
        that hand still sneaks food under the tray
                to feed
                or to get cleaned off
                            by an anxious tongue.

Your loyalty is commendable
                            and clearly established.

And the dog,
        like us,
                is glad you came.

INFANT DEVELOPMENT CENTER

1. INDIVIDUAL PROGRAM PLAN — STAFF EVALUATION

14 Months — The early childhood special education teacher describes Beth as alert and happy.
Beth's development scores are:

Assessment -		Gain in 7 mo.
Language	11 mo.	5 mo.
Social	16 mo.	5 mo.
Feeding	11 mo.	6 mo.
Cognition	10 mo.	5-6 mo.
Fine Motor	10-10½ mo.	6-6½ mo.
Gross Motor	9 mo.	4½-5 mo.

Parent Comments -
  Realistic, pleased with progress. Agree with test results.

2. STAFF COMMENTS   14 to 21 months.

9-12-77   Beth attending to toys and activities today. Observed a word approximation during session. Using spoon with assistance to feed self. Need to work on taking bites of cookie held.

10-3-77   Attended to toys and activities for short span of time. Easily distracted by noise and other children. Removed own socks with verbal and gestural encouragement. Moves forward to obtain object by scooting on hands and right lower extremity with left lower extremity tucked under her in a sitting position. Became cranky when attempts were made to change her to a hands and knees position for creeping.

10-17-77   Beth was easily distracted by other children and checked to see where her mother was. She discriminated ball twice and car once today. She loved looking at the book. We began activities standing but she lasted only a short time - preferred to finish the activities sitting down.

10-31-77   Beth showed spontaneous vocalizations throughout session. She repeated "Hi" throughout. Seemed to enjoy the socialization with Jennifer and Amy.

11-7-77   Beth continues to scoot in sitting. Maintenance of all-4's improved. Comes to stand with assist.

11-28-77   Beth had infected left eye and did not feel well today. Refused most activities or watched others.

12-12-77   Beth appears to be going thru astasia — no weight bearing on lower extremities. Beth was observed to creep reciprocally approximately 3 ft. without putting foot up to scoot. Difficult to interest in tilting activities.

12-19-77   Finger painted Christmas present — Beth did not like activity. Family left early for appointment.

1-9-78   Beth prefers right hand. Dislikes any physical prompts with activities. Imitating dog sound, cow and horse. Stacked 2 blocks one time.

1-9-78   Is creeping with correct reciprocal pattern, with less reversion to scooting in sitting. Still no interest in standing. Did stand briefly at table with therapist's support.

1-26-78   Seen individually for education. Throwing some objects in refusal to "give to worker." Some spontaneous babbling during session — no verbal imitation immediately after stimulus. Imitation of pat-a-cake one time. Responded to "no" — inhibited inappropriate behavior.

2-2-78   Observed more standing—two times independent standing for a few seconds. When presented initially with toy to left she would reach with the right, but when right is restrained for several trials she uses the left more frequently with and without restraint of right.

2-9-78   Independent attempts to get into vertical position with pulling to stand. Reaching with left is increased. More accuracy is observed in releasing with the left also.

2-23-78   Educational one-on-one session. Initial difficulty with sitting at floor table — needing physical assistance to attend and stay seated. Many distractions in the large room. Beth cried and screamed, refusing to cooperate with obstacle course, or any tilting on board, ball, or barrel.

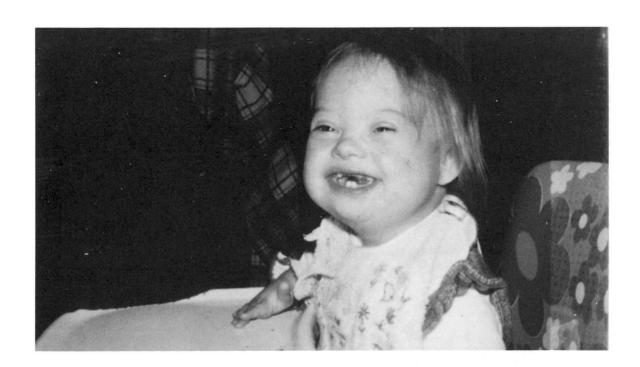

(Fourteen Months)

I hear myself saying
               lots of joy
                     about you, Kid.
And I mean it all.

But there are some shadows, too—
     personal shadows for me—
         ego shadows, for instance.

Through all my intense pride over being your father,
     I have
         my other moments.
Like
     when I talk about you and the "Mouse"
         both
            in one family,
         both
            flowing from me.

I wonder what thoughts
         what conclusions
               run through my listener's mind
                     about
                         my
                           defects.
One retarded child
         in a family
            draws some sympathy
               and support.
But two!
Is that excusable?
Does that change sympathy
            to suspicion?

Two!
     Yes, two—in one family.

What does that say to *them*
                                    about me?
                                    about my sperm?
                                    about my manhood?
Hey—
        I know it's silly
                                and unworthy of me
                                        and all that stuff,
        but being a person,
                                I've still got my ego
                                            to keep intact.

Sometimes I feel the need to quickly explain
        that my five "normal" children
                                        are "normal."
        all
                in the tops of their classes—
                        strong
                                healthy
                                        college-bound
                                        concerned
                                            beneficial to humankind
                                            special
                                            loving
                                            children-to-be-proud-of-types.

Sometimes I wish I could bring along
        one of my over-six-feet sons
        or one of my bright, attractive daughters
                just to show
                            that my sperm worked well
                                            most of the time.

Sometimes I find myself wanting to explain
        that my wife had severe food poisoning during the second month
                of her pregnancy with the "Mouse"

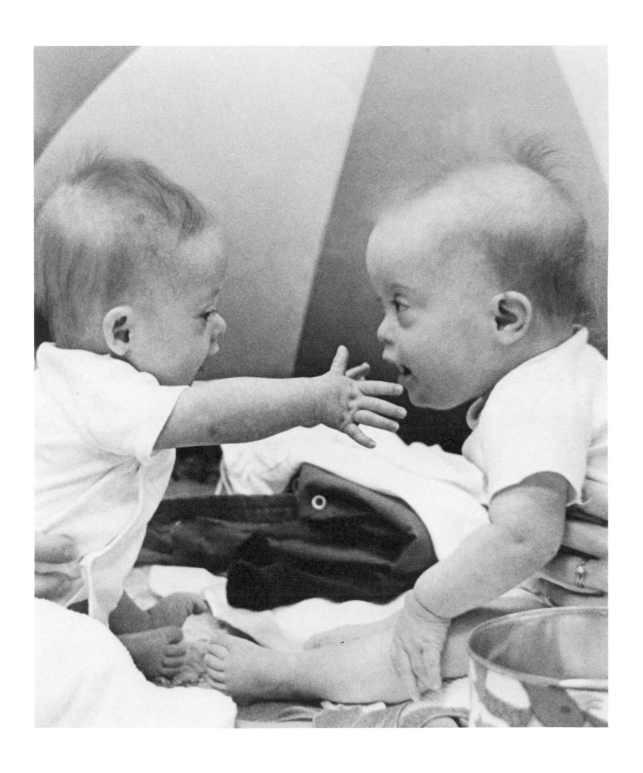

just to explain
    that it was no weakness
                  in us
    but just one of those strange, once-in-a-million happenings
      that happened
              to us —
                     twice
Sometimes I catch myself wanting to mention
    my paratrooper days
    degrees
    honors,
      just to remind others
                 that the retardation was a fluke—
                 that it doesn't run
                     in the family.

Sometimes I want to mention
          my brighter-than-me
          kinder-than-me
          more sensitive-than-me
              wife,
so that when these things are added up
            you will know
    that two retarded children
         throw no reflection
            on us.
That's my ego at work.
And while I want to share the joy of my two "special" children,
    I'm not always sure that I want to do it
          at the expense
            of my ego.

Damn.
    That's foolish!
But it's there—
    in the shadows.

We sure do love you, Pumpkin Face.
You have a way
        of throwing joy
           into
               any kind of a day.
That face of yours
        brightens up
        all
        the darknesses.
Your smile
    can happy up
        a whole crowd.

And who you are
        each today
      knocks the fears out of who you will be
                 in the distant
                    tomorrows.

(Sixteen Months)

Hey!
I think we've got
      the Mahalia Jackson
         of the Down's set.

Beth was itchy after supper.
    I got out the guitar
        to play some folk and country music.
She smiled.
    Then a gentle tapping of her hand
        began
          on her high chair.

The little body started to move
                              in a soft,
                                    quiet
                                          rhythm,
                        close
                        and intentionally to the beat.

She danced while sitting,
      gently lifting
                  one bottom cheek
                        then
                              the other.

Singing sounds came next—
                        more and more,
                        louder and louder,
                        happier and happier.
She slid forward,
      leaned back,
      threw her arms and legs out wide,
      flung back her head,
                  and sang
                  (showing all her teeth and tonsils)
                  at the top of her lungs—
                        long,
                              loud,
                                    happy sounds.

You've got music in you, Kid,
                  and it's fun!

Neat, Kid!
You get to be a baby
                a little longer
                      than most.
I love watching you learn
     and seeing you become consistent
                in some of your responses.
A "Hi, Beffy"
     is beginning to get
            a "Hi, Dad" back
                (even to Mom!).
A wave from me
     begets a wave from you
   and, of course, putting you down again
                 gets a complaint
     that eventually will go away
            when something else
                grabs your attention.
You will be our last baby
          and I must admit
     that I like the idea of getting
            more "baby"
              out of you,
   though I'm not nuts
        about what that will mean to *you*
                later on.

I do like the fact
     that the "baby" in you
          won't quit so soon.
I do like that
     until I remember the other side of the coin—
  the terrible twos
        may last three years,
 and (give us strength)
     you may stay a teenager
          longer
             than we can bear!

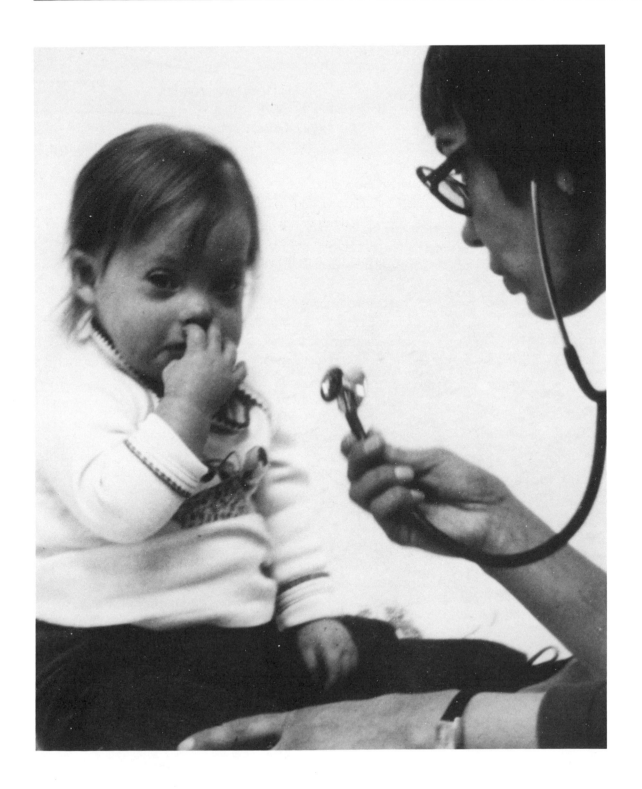

(Seventeen Months)

They say that it's part of the Down's nature
    that you are
        what they say you are—
            a sweet, loving, gentle child.
I know that.
I see it every day.
But what I don't want to talk about,
    I'd rather not face,
    I prefer not to consider,
   is that there may just be a whole other possibility
              to you.

There are glimpses,
        frightening glimpses,
   of a storm
      just beneath
        the surface of you;
   of a volcano
      just waiting
        for the right occasion
          to erupt;
   of dynamite
      searching
        for a match to light its fuse.

When I see you asleep
      and watch you love and play,
   I see that peace
      is a part of your makeup,
    and sweetness
      is who you are.

But, child,
    I'm always kept aware
      of the possibility
      of the suspicion

that somewhere,
        close inside,
                is a violence
                        waiting
                            to be turned loose.
Sometimes I see your emotions flip completely
        an instant from cuddle
                to anger—
        like someone flipped an on/off switch
                and changed you from complete light
                                        to instant dark.
And I wonder how far we are,
                you—and we—
                from destructive emotional eruptions
        that through your life
                will come and go—or worse—
                come and stay.

Just how thick is the shell
                that will keep the sweet you
                                        intact?

I find myself hoping
        that what I see
                is just what we
                        (in our advanced years of parenthood)
                                have spoiled you,
        and that what seems like a storm
                        is just a spoiled kid's normal reaction
                                to any displeasure.

That we can cure
                and we can live with.
But what if it's something deep,
                        and
                                with
                                        a tricky
                                            trigger?

(One and a Half Years)

Life
> just oozes out
>> all over you, Kid.

Sometimes your life
> invigorates mine
>> with a gentle touch

that awakens such good things
> in me.

Other times
> that life of yours
>> shouts out its presence
>>> with an exuberance

that seems almost
> illegal.

You do know how to fill a room, Kid.

Often,
> when I feel the pressures
>> of facing the rest of my life
>> of rearing another human being,

it dawns on me that the option is
> to spend that life
>> with a vacuum
>>> where you might have been.

In those moments,
> I count things.
> I count the steady joy,
>> the thousands of happies,
>>> the new purposes
>>>> and challenges,

                          the hugs,
                    the happy and tearful eyes,
                        the fulfilling
                            and surrounding love
                                    of you,
              and I can't help
                    but thank God
                            for *all* of it.

Shoot, Kid,
      we were going to be doing
                  something
                      with the rest of our lives.

      Why not
            do *you*?
It's sure better than doing life
                  without you!

"But I think they are wrong—
        she simply doesn't appear to have Down's.
            She's so alert
                  quick
                  bright
                  normal . . ."

I never know just how to handle words like these.

On the one hand, I'm proud—
                  proud that she's doing so well,
                  proud that she's keeping up
                      and so close to "normal,"
                  proud of the people who work so hard
                      to help her stretch herself.

Yet, on the other hand, aware—
           aware that she *does* have Down's
    and that
        nothing
            changes *that*.

I don't want to hide
        or disguise
           her Down's.

I'm not ashamed of it.
    (Yet why am I pleased when people tell me they wouldn't have
    known that she was a Down's child?)

I notice that
        (especially if they respond well to her)
    I *want* people to know that she's a Down's child,
        so that they know what kind of a person she is,
           how good she is for our world,
           that she's not to be feared,
           and that having a child like her
                is not to be feared.

I want them to know,
        through knowing her,
    that she's a person—
      a real, whole
          field for us to keep planting,
          row for us to keep hoeing,
          crop for us to keep harvesting
                person.
And a real, whole,
        planting,
        hoeing,
        and harvesting
          person
           in her own right.

I want them to know
        that this Downsy kid
                belongs with our world,
        that she lifts with us,
           cries with us,
           laughs with us,
           contributes with us,
           and takes with us,
   and that we need her
           and all those like her
               (and unlike her)
       to round out,
          sensitize,
          and humanize
            this world of ours.

(Eighteen Months)

So serious
      when your instructors
          tell,
            teach,
              move,
                and
                  love you
                    into your tomorrows.
These are things you must learn
      in order to function
         like other kids.
    —No, in order to be *you*—
       and to be the *most* you that's possible.

So obstinate,
    so hardheaded,

when their insistent "yes"
runs into
your insistent "no."

You must get that from your mother, Kid.
You surely don't get it from a sweet,
easygoing
guy
like me!

(Music Therapy Class)

Five squat, little
Down's syndrome
bodies,
with ten short,
stubby
arms,
circled in front of the mirror
listening intently
(almost too intently for 15-pound, 18-month-olds)
to instructions that they can't possibly
(can they?)
understand.

Bodies swaying and jiggling
to the beat of the music.
Shaking bells,
tapping sticks,
banging noisy things,
and loving the sound
and the feel
of it all.

There's rythm in each one of you
though certainly not
a unison rhythm
among the bunch of you.
Even so, you are a great little band.

I think we ought to sharpen you up,
take you on the road,
and call you
THE DOWNS BEATS.

How did you arrange
    to grow your teeth
        here and there
            around your mouth
    in the right places,
    but in the wrong sequence?

You started fine—
    one in the bottom middle,
    then one next to it.
But then you went crazy—
      teeth exploding all over your mouth—
    one in the back,
    one up top,
    another on the side.
And finally, they all came in,
        just right (eventually)
        beautiful,
        well-spaced,
        lined up.
    I never thought you'd do it!

Now, if your tooth *growing* caused us some consternation
    your tooth *testing* is what raised
        anxiety
          in your mother's heart.

Nursing a kid with ornery eyes like yours
        made her feel
    like a person
      who would purposely stick her finger
        on a moving power saw blade.

You didn't,
    we admit,
       use teeth as a weapon

until the second,
        jagged,
            little razortooth
                arrived.
I remember the day
        you looked into her eyes
        and without wavering,
            without passion,
decided to test her pain level.

Your two teeth
        sank into her nursing breast,
        and that moment,
            that day,
                that second,
    you brought an end
            to your
                nursing!

(Nineteen Months)

My daughter,
        who you are
            and
            what you are
    is far more important than
            who you are *not*
                and
                what you are *not*.

All of us are *not*
        things that we would like to be,
    and do not know
            things that we would like to know.

The difference between what *we*
              could be
              and know
              and do
                  is massive
                     for *all* of us.

Your difference
          is only
              a little more massive
                  than most of ours
              in the total scheme of things.
And yet,
            when it comes to potential,
        you are probably
              a lot closer to yours
                  than we are
                     to ours.
For you constantly try,
            persist,
            spend effort,
    where we are more likely to coast,
                relax,
                and settle for less.

If effort produces greatness,
     then you
            are one of the great,
    and I, child,
            am proud to have been given the gift
                  of being your father.

(Twenty Months)

Can *our* performance
                    close
                          some gaps?

How much of who *you* will be
                              depends
                                    on *our* efforts?

Years ago,
          they wrote off children like you early:
                    —short life span
                    —little accomplishments or mental growth
                    —eventual institutionalization
                    —lots of health problems
                    —they called you "Mongolian idiots."

But you had a very popular retardation,
          and a loving, learning way about you all.
     Study
          made knowledge about you easier.

So we learned,
          and found you to be learnable.
     But, still,
          we're only peering
                    through your dusk,
          and it's only through persistence
                              (ours *and* yours)
          that we have come this far.

Child,
     there's an uneasy tension between
                              pushing you
                              and accepting
                                   who *they* say you can be.

So we keep asking,
How much of your tomorrow
depends on our efforts
today?
If we simply
relax
our tension
will you have lost something
forever?
Will we have closed a door for you forever
simply by having failed to open it at the right moment?
How can we know
whether we are doing you love
or doing you damage?
Should we force ourselves
to force you more?

Should we pressure you more
to talk
to walk
to eat right
to use your fingers better
to listen and obey?

Don't you ever get to be
just a kid
growing gently
at your own pace?
Or must we make every act
(at least *almost* every act)
a learning,
correcting
experience?

Damn!
   I'd like
      —most of all—
         for you to be
           just a kid.

But I can't risk letting you
    when I know that might keep you
            from being just an adult
               some day.

INFANT DEVELOPMENT CENTER

Beth attends the Infant Development Center once a week receiving education and physical therapy. Attendance is regular.

The following changes are noted since the last evaluation:

Language:
- imitates words inexactly
- uses gestures and other movements to communicate
- with prompting, uses single words to express wants
- follows the simple direction "give me"

Social:
- often clings to or pushes away adults
- sometimes cries when preferred activity is blocked
- picks up and puts away toys on request
- independently chooses toy and begins to play
- mimics domestic activities
- usually plays near other children, demonstrating limited interaction at this time.

Eating:
- feeds self with spoon - many spills
- chews well
- continues to need assistance with cup drinking

Toileting:
- fusses to be changed when diapers are soiled
- bowel movements are regular

Dressing:
- pulls off hat, socks, and other simple garments upon request
- cooperates in dressing by moving arms and legs
- attempts to brush hair when presented a brush
- imitates simple grooming actions

Cognition:
- finds the toy hidden under one of several cloths, when object is of interest to the child
- familiar gesture imitation continues with consistency, new and unfamiliar gestures are inconsistently imitated

Beth is a 21 month old girl. According to the Michigan Developmental Profile, she is functioning at the following levels:

1. Individual Program Plan   21 months

Assessments: age	21 mo.	gain in 6½ mo.
Language	15 mo.	4 mo.
Social	27 mo.	11 mo.
Self-help feeding	13.5 mo.	2.5 mo.
Self-help toileting	16 mo.	4 mo.
Self-help dressing	16-17 mo.	5 mo.
Cognitive	12 mo.	2 mo.
Fine motor	15-19 mo.	5-7 mo.
Grcss motor	11.4-12.6 mo.	2-3 mo.

Beth cooperative through evaluation. Creeping independently, but prefers to scoot on her bottom. Is walking holding on to furniture for 1-2 steps. Lowers self from standing to sitting by plopping on her bottom. All reflexes are present and normal for her age.

2. Staff Comments   21 to 27 mo.

3-14-78   Beth's sister brought her to school today—Mother is ill. During education Beth elicited "car" several times after verbal model by worker. Beth attended 30 minutes without moving away from sitting table. Beth would pretend that she was throwing several times, but would not drop object.

3-14-78   Beth pulled to stand, ½ kneel on right into stand, independently. Resisted squat to stand. Took 1 step to right while standing at table. Little cooperation with other activities. Cried during tilting activities.

4-3-78   Beth began to warm up half-way through session. Some verbalizing but not spontaneous. Liked "Ernie" doll — hugged, combed hair and gave kiss. Completed circle puzzles but did avoidance behavior.

4-25-78   Mom sat in therapy session today to see if it would keep Beth from crying. Beth went through obstacle course once requiring much verbal coaching. Worked on ½ kneel to stand and squat to stand, however, Beth continues to put more weight on right lower extremity. Beth creeps independently but will sit-crawl on smooth surface.

5-2-78   Mother's group. Talked about changes in feeling with time and excellent early care at KUMC. Family going camping over Memorial Day with other families with handicapped children.

5-30-78   Demonstrated some screaming behavior with play activities. Responded to verbal correction and stopped inappropriate behavior. Touched 4 basic facial parts on verbal command.

6-13-78   Beth performed obstacle course with verbal and physical assistance. No crying was elicited. Sat on tilt board with some assist to keep her on, would not stand or kneel.

6-13-78   Beth looked at approximately 30 pictures — naming about 5; actions with name.

9-11-78   Ambulation unstable at times with some falling. Standing from squat. Sitting from standing without problems. Left, right, forward protective extension elicited in sitting, prone, supine. Right-hand dominance but would use left if prompted. Very curious. Much verbal communication — jabbering.

(Two Years)

Labels—
        should we work to eliminate them?

The label
        "Down's"
                immediately categorizes her
                        in our minds.

It says things to us
        that put her in "her box":
                retarded
                limited
                sentenced for life
                unable to perform like us
                not "normal"
        and it evokes responses
                that cause people to treat her differently.

Playing with her last night she seemed
        so like our other kids at two—
                happy
                    funny
                        teasy
                            inventive
                              sharp
                                pesty.

We work to stretch her limits
        yet the label
                always reminds us
                conditions us
                screams at us
        that she has limits
                that many of us
                      don't
                        have.

So I have to ask,
   are the labels
      part of the limiters?
  Or are they simply a way of reminding us
        who she is
        and who she can become?

Do we use labels to force us to face her real limits,
    the ones we know belong to Down's
        and these alone?
Or do we let them put other limits on her
        that she shouldn't
       mustn't
        be hindered by?
If labels describe limits,
   shouldn't we *all* have labels
      that describe
      our handicaps?
He/she is:
    unable to relate
    selfish
    closed-minded
    brilliant, but not nice
    a turkey
    or lots of others.

Are labels
  derogatory
    or helpful?

If I had a label to define my handicaps
        what would the label be?
  How would it affect society's expectations of me?
  How would my label affect my expectations
        of myself?

"How,"
        someone asked at a parent's meeting,
                            "Do you justify the sacrifices?
        How do you justify the extra money,
                    time,
                    effort,
                    agony,
                    and love
    that retarded children
                syphon away
                        from the rest of your family?"

The question caught me by surprise.
Even though Matthew (microcephalic) had been with us for years,
        and Beth was now a fixture in our lives,
        and Mom-Mom (with arteriosclerosis) had lived with us
                                    almost forever,

I confess I didn't think of them in terms of
                            our
                        sacrifice.
I do remember wishing things were easier for
                        them
                            sometimes.
But I never remember spending much time
        wishing that things were easier for *us*
                    as far as they were concerned.
Now that I think about the question,
        it seems that the ultimate answer to that concern
            would be to hope
                    for their deaths,
            and we kept hoping
                    for their lives—continuing
                and as full
                    as we could help them be.

Understand,
      we were always faced
            with the *possibility*
                   of their deaths,
     (constantly, with the "Mouse"
             and eventually, with Mom),
    but we didn't think of it as solution
               to our special times
                   of caring.

I asked each of our other children
    what they thought
           about what they had to give up
              for the "Mouse,"
           and about what they might have to give up
              for Bethy.

They all responded the same way.
    They didn't think of them in terms
               of any personal cost.
    They thought, instead,
             of what they had received,
             and of what the others had meant
             to them.

There was some slight difference in their attitude toward Mom-Mom,
    but the overriding feeling was
             that they loved her,
             and that she needed us,
    and that even in the bad days
             we needed her
                in our lives.

Maybe,
    just maybe,
           our children's response to these special people

has to do with the tone we parents set
even before they become a part
of our lives,
and with the values we put on other human beings
no matter what their situation might be.

People are gifts.
And a gift should be seen
as a gift.

It loses too much joy
when we only concentrate
on the problems
that gift
might bring.

INFANT DEVELOPMENT CENTER

1. INDIVIDUAL PROGRAM PLAN—STAFF EVALUATION

27 months
Assessments:

		gain in 6 mo.
Language	24 mo.	9 mo.
Social	28 mo.	1 mo.
Self-help feeding	16 mo.	2½ mo.
Self-help toileting	16 mo.	0 mo.
Self-help dressing	19 mo.	2-3 mo.
Cognitive	18 mo.	6 mo.
Fine Motor	23½ mo.	4 mo.
Gross Motor	16 mo.	3 mo.

Parents' concern: Increase schedule to twice a week. Are not concerned about toileting unless staff is. Beth doesn't eat well.

The speech therapist describes Beth's receptive language skills (or what she is understanding) at the 24 mo. level. Beth can:
1. follow 2 simple commands.
2. select 2 named objects out of a group of 3 objects.
3. show body parts, toys, and items of clothing on request.

STAFF COMMENTS   27 mo. to 33 mo.

9-25-78   Beth was in education for ½ hr. with Stacy. She worked well for about 45 minutes. She and Stacy imitated each other in activities.

10-6-78   Introduced "me" with ball play and function or action cues with ball and car. Some crying with Mother in room.

10-16-78   Little crying today—good cooperation. Gait pattern improved with low guard of upper extremities. Good titling reactions in sitting and 4-point position. Up and down stairs with better coordination using railing and minimum assistance by therapist.

10-30-78   Good naming of associated pairs. Tolerated well for tactile cues on hard palate and attempted tongue elevation.

11-6-78   Increased understandable verbalizing. Attempted balance beam and jumping activities. Increased cooperation.

11-10-78   Added "I like food" pictures with Beth naming object. Some difficulty for imitation of sounds.

11-13-78   Good fine motor responses — blocks, beads, pegs, storybook. Good cooperation on tilt board in sitting and standing with assist.

11-20-78   Continued imitation of isolated sounds p, b, t, s, with good response. Following directions.

12-4-78   Recorded naming pictures; good re-auditorization on playback.

12-11-78   Very cooperative today. Good attention to small motor tasks.

12-18-78   Group with Stacy. Excellent response for naming pictures and following directions for on-in-under.

1-8-79   Good attention span. Beth seemed glad to be back!

1-17-79	Beth worked on counting 1-5 today and identifying picture cards by object use.
1-17-79	Repetitive syllable drill with good imitation of 2 syllables.
1-22-79	Performed obstacle course with minimum to moderate assistance.
2-14-79	Worked at table 40 mins. Activities included: block/made train; spontaneous simple strokes with crayon, both right and left; Maximum assistance matching colors; Moderate assistance matching pictures/objects; auditory recall good with 2 objects. Very cooperative. Counts rote 1-6 spontaneously.
2-12-79	Good 2-word phrases; spontaneous speech becoming more intelligible; good imitation of 2-syllable sequences. Introduced yes-no concept with fair response.
2-21-79	Performed obstacle course 2 times in 4-5 min. each time. Propelled scooter board in sitting a short distance.
2-28-79	Seen for education alone — great! Beth remembered picture she drew last session was of Claudia (Beth's sister).
3-5-79	Continues with good responding for agent-action and action-agent imitation. Also good naming without visible cues and response to "what" questions.

(Two and a Half Years)

Music
        and dance
        and feelings
                    just seem to explode
                            from you.
In the morning,
            alone in your room,
                    we hear your soft,
                            waking
                                chatter.

You have lots of gentle things
                    to explain to your dolls
                            and to the animals
                                on the wallpaper.
Then comes the quiet singing—
                    tunes and songs unrecognizable
                            (to us anyway).
You have a way
            of steadily
                getting
                    louder.
We open the door a crack
            to watch and hear.

You stand,
        then sway.
Soon your arms are raised
                high over your head
            and, like a Hallelujah Honey,
                your body moves
                        all over the crib
                and the singing
                        is at the top of your lungs.

You break us up, child.
Such joy
        is
              contagious.
Sometimes,
        just five minutes of you
                is worth the total
    of the two and one-half years
           of the pains and scares
              we sometimes feel.
You have a way of paying off—
           of giving us
              more
                than we can ever
                  give you.

So, Little Three Eyes,
        the repairs to your original equipment
                have already started.
Your eyes didn't start their occasional wandering
           and crossing
              until recently,
      and they tell us
         we've got to try to correct it now
        before you get used to seeing
            two visions
      and then
        tuning
         one out.
So,
    we shift the flesh-colored patch
      (it makes it look like the skin grew over one eye)
        from one eye to the other.

That patch,
      combined with the bifocals,
    makes you look like
          a tiny,
            scholarly
              pirate.
But without those things,
    you just look like
          a cute,
            little,
              cross-eyed kid.

You are so good
    about the patch
        that keeps your eye from drifting.
We know you hate it,
        especially when it has to be
            ripped off.
You complain.
    You let us know you'd rather not have to deal with it.
      But you obey
        and try to hold still
           when we put it on
           or take it off.
For an impatient kid,
        you certainly are patient
            about this!
You are almost as good
        about
          the funny little bifocals
    which immediately get fogged
        and blocked
          with fingerprints,
          cracker crumbs,
          jelly,
          juice,
          bananas,
          and badly aimed kisses.

Now and then we see
                    that you have taken them off
        and then
            the frantic search
                        begins.
You cooperate about as well
                    as Bugs Bunny
                            with Elmer Fudd.
So *we* hunt.

First, the logical places—
                    "Where was she last?"
            Look *on* things—
                        nothing.
            Look *under*.
                    Behind?
                        Nothing.
            Look *in* things.
            Turn things over.
            Check other rooms.
            Check other floors.
            Check other *countries*??
Finally,
        much later,
                after we've given up
                        (but not yet ordered a new pair)
                they are found!
                        in a wastebasket
                            in another room
                    or behind some boxes
                            in the back shed.
            Geez!

The glasses
        do
        make her noticeable—
    that tiny little kid
                with bifocals.

People stop and take a second look
and say things to her
and to each other *about* her
with caring smiles.
At first,
the idea of the glasses gave me some problems.
How could a doctor possibly know
what a two-year-old can see
or how clear the images were
at different distances?
Was he just trying to sell another pair of glasses?
What if he was way off with his guesswork
and the glasses were wrong
and *hurting* her sight?
Jeanne took Beth to him
and was amazed,
pleased,
satisfied
with his technical skills,
ingenious tests,
and unique equipment.
And the glasses certainly keep her eye from wandering,
and she seems to feel comfortable wearing them,
and she acts like she sees better with them,
so—
I guess they are doing her
a lot
of good.
We'll see.

INFANT DEVELOPMENT CENTER

INDIVIDUAL PROGRAM PLAN—STAFF EVALUATION

Child's Name: Bethany Bakely   Entry Date: 7/15/76

DOB: 6/14/76   IPP Conference Date: 3/20/79

Coordinator: Lee Ann Britain   Recorder: Susan Cannon

Persons Attending -

    Child's Family: Rev. Don and Jeanne Bakely (Parents)

    IDC Staff: Melanie Ryding (Speech Therapist), Susan Cannon (Physical Therapist), Joan Rosenberg (Early Education Teacher), Lee Ann Britain (Director)

Assessments:		Gain in 6 mos.
C.A. 33 mo.		
Language	31 mo.	7 mo.
Social	35 + mo.	7 mo.
Self-help feeding	30 mo.	14 mo.
Self-help toileting	23 mo.	7 mo.
Self-help dressing	24 mo.	5 mo.
Cognition	33 mo.	15 mo.
Fine motor	23 mo.	2-5 mo.
Gross motor	19-21 mo.	5-5.5 mo.

Parent's concern: "The next step after here"

Long Term Goal: Placement in pre-school program meeting Bethany's individual needs.

Short Term Goals: (1) Increase block building, (2) Increase paper/pencil tasks, (3) Improve manipulation of pencil, (4) Increase balance reactions in standing, (5) Improve coordination. (6) Continue sound imitation and reinforce jargon patterns with phrases which appear to be uttered. (7) Develop auditory memory for following two-part directions and repeating two associated items. (8) Continue sound sequence imitation. (9) Improve dressing and undressing skills, (10) Improve toileting skills, (11) Continue improvement of problem solving skills.

Plan: Continue IDC for Physical Therapy once a week — Speech and Education twice a week.

Your signature indicates you have participated in this conference regarding your child.

Parent's Signature [Jeanne F. Bakely] Date March 20, 1979

Parent's Signature [Donald C. Bakely]

cc: Parents
    Dr. R. Kauffman

STAFF COMMENTS   33 to 39 mo. of age.

3-26-79   Beth was sick last week. Beth refused many tasks by saying "no." After worker responded with "Yes," she would say "OK." Work was fair — Beth into playing games.

4-2-79   For first time, Bethany spontaneously responded with "Bethany here." Cues necessary for response to "what doing" with action picture.

4-11-79   Beth refused counting activities—until worker did them.

4-11-79   Good phrases associated with picture naming and locating 1 or 2 action pictures.

4-25-79   Beth's preacademic skills include: (1) Name numbers 1-9. (2) Name letters B and Y. (3) Name circle, triangle, and square.

4-30-79	Comprehension tasks for "What doing" with cues. Good response for big/little pictures.
5-2-79	Performed ball gymnastics with assist necessary to stay on ball. Beth sat on tilt board without assist and rocked self independently. Assist necessary on all-4's and in standing.
5-2-79	Beth recognized the following names: Bethany, Lois, Claudia, Mommy, Daddy.
5-7-79	Bethany getting noncompliant at times. Minor success by giving her two acceptable activities to choose from and letting her decide what to do.
5-14-79	Introduced Mother-Baby animal picture series; continues good naming.
5-16-79	Performed tumbling activities on mat—rolling, somersaults, climbing over barrels and wedges with physical assist. Attempted somersaults without assist—appeared to enjoy activities.
5-23-79	Worked on tracing shapes (connecting dotted lines) — minimal assistance given.
6-19-79	Imitation of verb(ing) with fairly good articulation.
6-22-79	Locating 1 or 2 action pictures with agent-action cues, then repeat phrase with good intell. Drill stereotype phrase "I see _____" with minimum cues. Good intell. Locating objects on/under table or chair with minimum prompts.
7-3-79	Beth forgot glasses. Located animal, food pictures. Naming pictures with I action _____.
7-6-79	Worked in a group for speech, education and perceptual motor. Named objects out of sight by touch and differentiated pictures of nouns.
7-17-79	Good isolated /s/w/ tactile cues on tongue midline and for teeth closure.

(Three Years)

You like you,
        don't you, Kid!
You like what you see in the mirror
                              at home,
                              in department stores,
                              in shiny metal table legs,
                              and every place you see your image
                                        played back to you.

You play with that kid in the mirror,
      dance with her,
      cheer her on,
      try out faces on her,
      and experiment with her eyes,
                       mouth,
                       gestures,
                       and expressions.

You like your pictures
      and
            what you see of you
                     in other people's joy.

If there's one thing I'd like to keep giving you, my child,
                                  it's *that*.
I want to give you
           (as much as I can)
                    a life of being comfortable
                            with being *you*.
You have that now—
                in spades!
We,
      and those who know you,
                   make
               that
                 easy.

But the moments are soon to come
    when others will try
        to wrench
           that feeling
                away from you.
And we who love you
        are going to have to work hard
                and fast
    to make your joy of who you are
            strong
            and solid
            and thick
            and deep
            and real enough
    that no one can shout it
        or taunt it
            out of you.
Look, Sweety,
    I know we can't *protect* you
            from what people
                —almost naturally—
                    will say.
I don't want to build a wall
        to keep unkind words
            from you.
    These words will come.
        They will be a part
            of living
                for you.
The question is:
    how do I prepare you
        not
            to be wounded
                by them?
    How do I help you know
        that what someone else's prejudice says
                about your worth

is not the same as what God
and *knowing* people
say?
How do I help you feel as good about you
as God and the people who know you
feel
about you,
rather than letting your attitude
reflect
and accept
what some unloving people
might say
or feel?
So far,
our enjoying of you
has set the tone
for your acceptance
of yourself.
And that
will be sufficient
while you are surrounded
by us
and our friends.
But will it be enough
to get you ready,
for instance,
for the first time
that you get on a non-school bus
by yourself?
Will it be enough
for the first time
you spend some hours
out of our sight
and our protection
only with *others*
on your *own*?

I think the reason
            you
                        are taking so long
                                    in going to the potty
                                                alone
            is that
                        you like the cheering
                                    that accompanies
                                                each success
            while
                        your tinkling
                                    is still a family encouraged,
                                                family accompanied
                                                            activity.
Shoot,
            I've seen that bathroom more crowded
                                    with more cheering
                                                and excitement
                        than we usually have
                                    at a family birthday party.
I never saw anybody use the "potty moments"
                                    to milk
                                                as much applause
                                                            as you do.
Cheering, encouragement, and urging lead
                                    to one squirt
                        which buys
                                    a lot of cheering and congratulations
                                                            for you.
                                    "Good girl, Beff!" "Yea, Beff!"
You smile—
                        proud,
                                    looking from face to face
                                                basking in the rewards
                        that come from such
                                    great
                                                accomplishments.

Then,
    "Gonna do a little more, Beth?"
            —Squirt—
        More cheers, more applause.
"A little more, Beff?"
            —Squirt—
               smile
                   applause.
If the applause isn't quite up to your level of expectation,
    you ask,
        "Beffie good girl?"
               and we make the cheering
                        right!
That's good
        for the final squirt.
Then
        you head off for wherever you were going
            before you got interrupted
                for your role
                   in "potty theater."
It's a triumphal march
           for you.
        Ringing in your ears are the cheers
           and still the conversation continues
               as adults explain to the new arrivals
               and they, in turn,
                   offer their congratulations.

I think there should be an award
               for "Best Potty Act"
        or at least
               for "Best Family Reaction."
        We've got potential winners
               in
                   this
                     house.

"I gonna *git* you!"
That's her signal for me to shriek
"Oh, no!"
and hide
in some
obvious
spot.

Kid,
    you run just like you walk—
        same speed.
The only way we can tell it's running
      is that
        your face and arms
           run
while your body
    waddles
      at its normal walking speed
        —just with more excitement
          than pure walking.
When I see you run,
    I think you must have taught
      Daisy Duck
        her style.

Eventually,
    as I did with the other kids,
      I let you catch me
        for reward.
    But that's always the wrong thing to do.
      It disappoints,
        disgusts,
        and even angers you
    And then it's your turn to say, "Oh, no!"

You don't seem to know what to do
      when you catch me.
    You are different from the other kids.
      You seem more comfortable with the chase
        than with the catch.
But, Kid,
    I've *got* to let you catch me.
After all,
    how long can a fifty-year-old man run
      from a three-year-old
        waddler?

Doubt
      is not
            your major problem, Kid.

When a choice is offered,
      your mind responds
                  with the quickness
                  and the force
                  and the finality
                        of a mousetrap.
Getting *your* decision
                  to correspond
                        to *my* decision
            is where the heads butt,
                  and where,
                        I'm afraid,
                        I'm going to spend much of my
                              getting-old
                                    energy.
It seems
            the only time your decision
                        is slower than a bullet,
                        or more moveable
                              than Mount Rushmore
            is when your computer mind
                        scans the air
                        and senses strong conflict
                              with your parents.
Normally that doesn't bother you
      unless you sense
                  that you really aren't
                        going
                              to win.
We notice that
                  if we want a "Yes"
                  and you want a "No,"

you,
        in your unique way,
                negotiate.
You hem,
you haw,
you ignore,
        walk away,
                change the subject,
                        distract,
                                point at this,
                                        suggest that,
tease,
        cry,
                ignore,
                        do something else,
                                tell us you have to go potty,
                                        grab a book,
                                                watch TV,
                                                        wiggle your eyelashes,
                                                                giggle and run,
                                                                        use your cute,
                                                                                use your anger,
                                                                                        cry,
                                                                                                con,
                                                                                                        explain,
        jump in somebody elses' arms,

        jabber with enough seriousness that we think you really are trying to
tell us something,
        ask for a hug,
                ask for a kiss,
                        ask for a drink
        or
                all
                        of the above—
                                or
                                        whatever.

They tell me,
        and I read in the papers,
    that the Vietnam peace talks were tough.
Maybe
    we should have sent
        only negotiaters
          who had reared
            three-year-old Down's kids.
At least *they*
      would have been
        prepared.

The impediment
      in your speech
        is more obvious to me
           than it is
            to you.
You jabber on
      without stopping,
      completely serious,
      obviously enjoying our (your) conversation,
      assuming (with no question) that I simply understand
        or agree,
      telling stories of the day's happenings
        or of things you want to relive.
When you do get very intentional
       and deliberate with your words—
          saying them slowly,
            loudly,
          in syllables,

you seem to do it more
                        because you feel I
                                    have a hearing defect
                        than because *you*
                                    have a speech problem.
Sometimes you say words
                        right in my face
                                    patiently
                                    insisting
                                    forcefully
                        even holding my cheeks
                        and making sure my eyes
                                    are following your mouth.
Just like your teacher,
            you do it over and over
                        until you assume I have it,
                        or until you give up.
Sometimes you tease.
        You make up a word,
                    try to teach it to me,
                    and when I repeat it,
                                you break up in laughter.
Geez, kid,
            you
                    are
                        fun
                            to raise.

INFANT DEVELOPMENT CENTER

INDIVIDUAL PROGRAM PLAN—STAFF EVALUATION

Child's Name: Bethany Bakely
Entry Date: 7-15-76
DOB: 6-14-76
IPP Conference Date: 10-25-79
Coordinator: Joan Rosenberg
Recorder: Joan Rosenberg
Persons Attending -
   Child's Family: Rev. Donald and Jeanne Bakely (Parents)
   IDC Staff: Melanie Ryding (Speech Pathologist), Lee Ann Britain (Director), Joan Rosenberg (Early Education Teacher)

Assessments:		*Gain in 6 mos.*
C.A. 39 mo.		
Preschool Expressive	33.0	7½
Language Scale Receptive	40.5	1½
Social		
Self-help feeding	36	
Self-help toileting	28-31	
Self-help dressing	24-27	
Cognition	3 yrs. 2 mo.-6 yrs. 0 mo.	
Fine motor		
Gross motor		

Parent's Concern:

Long Term Goal: Placement in Public School Program when age appropriate.

Short Term Goal: (1) Improve dressing skills. (2) Improve expressive description of object functions. (3) Develop counting skills 1-10. (4) Demonstrate understanding of time concepts—today, tomorrow, and yesterday. (5) Increase number of quantitive concepts understood. (6) Increase vocabulary of understanding for item functions, category labels, actions, concepts (locations, size, shape, color, other descriptions). (7) Reinforce phrase structure and emphasize imitation of short sentence structure. (8) Develop short-term memory for following directions and repeating a series of two and three associated items.

Plan: Continue I.D.C. Integrated Preschool Class.
Your signature indicates you have participated in this conference regarding your child.
Parent's Signature: Donald C. Bakely   Date:
Parent's Signature: Jeanne F. Bakely   Date: 10/25/79
cc: Parents
    K.U. Pediatric Clinic

STAFF COMMENTS   39 mo. to 4 yrs.

9-18-79   Attending preschool II. Great day.

10-2-79   Beth did not follow directions well — stubborn! She pretends not to hear you speak to her.

10-4-79   Good responding during group speech in Preschool II. Cautious for tactile stimulation with shaving cream.

11-13-79   Toilet training going well. Good day.

11-15-79   Recorded N + is(ing) with reinforce of objective phrase and 2-part associated item recall.

12-4-79   Worked on Christmas decorations today. Began singing Christmas songs. Not as verbal as past sessions—maybe due to being absent for 2 previous sessions.

12-11-79   Beth very stubborn today—saying "No" to tasks and rolling on the floor during music! Toilet training going well.

12-18-79   Went to Santa's House — fun day!

1-7-80   Fair response for verb(ing) phrase completion; locating 2 or 3 pictures delayed, accurate. Sent home pictures for plural markers.

1-14-80   Beth into saying no! to activities and questions. She does well when activity is presented anyway.

2-4-80   Emphasized I want _____, please with training cards with good imitative response. Beth appeared not to be hearing accurately as noted in /sh, ch, s/ production.

2-18-80   Very affectionate — did well on general information questions. Attended perceptual motor group.

2-29-80   Great paper/pencil tasks on pre-academic skills — matching number to number of objects and horizontal and vertical same pictures. Good attention.

3-14-80   Fair response for locating two pictures from multiple array. Good response for choosing category pictures.

4-25-80   Good day—attended well.

5-2-80   Pix for and assoc. with opposites up-down; hot-cold; day-night with good response for first two sets.

6-9-80   Beth required prompting to participate in majority of activities. Performed obstacle course and swinging. Refused scooterboard.

6-13-80   Good cooperation in class — did not want to go to PM Group. Celebrated Beth's birthday today!

6-27-80   Six month speech and education re-evaluation today.

(Three and a Half Years)

How could so much love
                    be jammed
                              into such
                                    a teeny
                                        package?
You haven't got
                that
                    much body, Kid.

You are little,
            small,
                    squished, even.

And I don't mean little
                because
                        you're a three-year-old,
        I mean little
            for
                    a three-year-old.

Yet,
        you've got a personality
                    and a presence
                            that fills
                                any room you enter.

And you've got a force of love—
                        an acting,
                        attacking,
                        comin' at you,
                        comin' all *over* you
                                    love
        that seems like it's more than enough
                            for a three-hundred-pounder.

When I look at you,
        it makes me think
    that, perhaps,
        the One who packs love
      is still trying to show us
        just what pure love
            is like—
    how powerful
      a small cupful
            of it
              can be—
    how far
      a little of it
          can go.
You see,
    the world
      has had its Einsteins
            Copernicuses,
              Aquinases,
                Michelangelos,
                Moseses,
                  Wyeths,
    to make itself
      technologically
        and artistically
            correct.
But to make it
      more *livable*,
    God sprinkles it
      —sometimes *stuffs* it—
          with those who love:
          Jesus,
            Francis of Assisi
            Barnabas,
              Martin Luther King, Jr.
              and a constant
                always
                  flow

                                                    of kids
                                                        like
                                                            you.

With kids like you,
        God
                keeps
                        shoving love at us
                                in its simplest,
                                        purest,
                                        least contaminated,
                                        least complicated
                                                        form.
And it's the kind of love we need
        in this complex,
                tricky,
        contaminated world
                        of confused relationships.

And, Kid,
        I'm glad God dropped
                        you off
                                in my century
                                in my town
                                    at
                                            my
                                                house.

How come things work
              so funny with you, Kid?
Like the way
        sweat
              affects your speech.
It makes your glasses
              slip down your face
                    and pinch off
                          that nothin' nose
                                of yours,
        and *that*
              makes you
                    talk
                          funny.

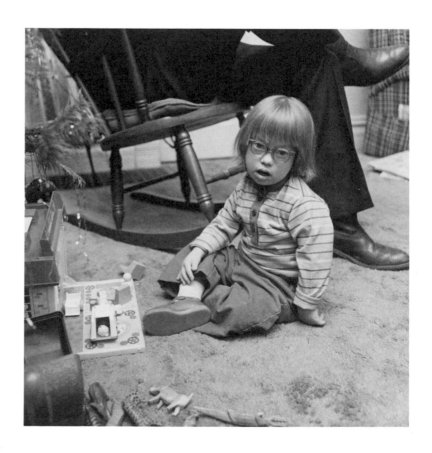

I know folks
would like me to use
a better word
to describe you, Kid,
but the word that seems
to fit my needs
and do the job
(even with all the other possible words considered)
is
fun.
You're
fun,
Kid.

When you wake up in the morning,
when your face and body run to me at the end of a working day,
when we laboriously go through all your play routines,
when you supply the melody as I sing you to sleep,
and even when you supply us with the wrong note
to sing our grace at meals—
the word that fits most,
that hits you right on the nose
is
fun.
You bring a special
warm
lots-of-laughing
happiness
into our lives,
and that's called
fun.

During "Sesame Street"
    is not
            the time
                    to try to attract
                            your attention.
You are so mesmerized
    that I have to turn off the set
                    to get your attention.

But Sesame Street does a job
    and you remember
            and learn
                    things that keep slipping back
                                    into
                                        your
                                        living skills.
So many people
    so many groups
            are helping you to be
                    as much *you*
                            as possible.
And I'm grateful.

INFANT DEVELOPMENT CENTER

Age 4 - 5 yr.

Excerpt of comments from progress notes:

Started new preschool group. Entered class with no hesitation.
Speech session and emphases on noun plus verbs with -ing endings.
Wore eye patch — to have surgery at end of month.
Beth needs maximum assistance to cut out 4" circle—pastes cut shapes independently.
Beth recognizes and names letters A-Z.
Arrived in bad mood — says "I can't," but then was cooperative.
Beth completes worksheet and enjoys independent drawing. Beth does not return to preschool classroom, worker finds her in secretary's office. Beth answers "I don't know" when questioned about where she should be.
Cooperative. Followed group directions. Assist classmates in complying to directions.

Excerpts from Preschool Teacher's report:

Bethany Bakely was reevaluated in May 1981 to assess her progress since her evaluation in August 1980. Beth was cooperative and enthusiastic during the evaluation.

Beth passes all items through the five year level except one item at the 3½ to 4 year level — Indicate number of halves in a whole. Beth recognized A-Z shown in random order. She is beginning to relate words she knows that start with the letters—i.e.: "B starts my name."

For summer, teacher recommends continuation of alphabet identification, number concepts 1-10 and continuation of number identification 1-20. Beth should be encouraged to write her name using upper and lower case letters.

Excerpts from Physical Therapist's report: Evaluated previously only in fine motor.

Fine Motor — Beth has difficulty with skills of tracing, coloring, copying and cutting. General manipulative skills are good.

Gross Motor — She is hesitant, does not like to take chances, does not use alternate feet on stairs, jump, hop or stand on 1 foot. Throwing skills are quite good. Equilibrium in walking is good, starting to run, although still a bit awkward.

Scores	Previous	Present	Gain
Fine Motor	4 ¼ yr.	5 yr.	¾ yr.
Gross Motor	4 yr.	4 ¼ yr.	¼ yr.

Recommendation: Appropriate school placement.

(Four Years)

When I watch you, Kid,
when I see you move,
    and think,
        and plan,
            and invent,
                and con,
                    and play,
                        and procrastinate,
                    and teach,
                    and act,
                      and tease,
                      and listen,
                        and cajole,
                        and cry,
                        and laugh,
                          and count,
                          and read,
                            and love,

    it's hard for me to believe
        that a little sharpie
            like you
                is going to be
                    retarded.
Listen to me—!

I even have to force myself to remember
    that the words
        "going to be"
            are already
                wrong.
The fact is,
    you always were
    you always *are*
    you always will be
        retarded.

They don't have a pill,
       or a process,
       or an operation,
       or even a revolution,
              that will make you
                  "un-Down's."
They just have ways
       to make you
           less imprisoned
              by it.
But it will always be there.
           You got it
            You've had it.
            You'll keep it.

OK—even though I know all that
          and accept it,
            I've still
              got
                a problem.
     The problem is
          that even though I know
              you are retarded,
     "retarded"
          simply isn't the word
              that describes you
                  best.
     "Beth" is.

And being Beth
        seems so right
        and so natural
           for you,
    that most of the time
           nothing else
              seems out of place.

In fact,
     the only thing that seems out of place
                            when I'm with you,
     is the word "retarded."

When the word is tacked on to you
      it somehow makes us stop seeing you as a person
              —as Beth—
                  a neat, natural kid.

The word turns us
          from who you are
                    to what you've *got*.
And who you *are*,
          Bethany Flagg Bakely,
     is more important
              than any condition
                   that affects
                      you.

(Four Years)

Derek,
    in your class,
        has ears
            that don't work.

So your teacher, Joan,
           learns to "sign" with her hands.
    And you kids pick it up
           just like
            it came naturally.

Your sister Lois
    buys you a kid's book on "signing."

It amazes me
    how you remember the words
        describing the signs under the pictures.
You've got
    a remarkable memory.
I've noticed, though,
        that the whole batch of kids
           in your class
  slur the signs
        just like you slur
          your speech.

Little hands and fingers zip
        somewhere near
           where they are supposed to,
  and Joan goes nuts
      figuring out
      what you are trying
        to say.

She's retarded.
    Yet at four years
        she knows her alphabet,
                small and large letters,
                        by sight and memory.
        She counts past twenty,
            can tell me some larger numbers by sight,
            can read lots of words by memory
                        (not by figuring them out),
            knows the colors
                    and has words for most things she sees.
        She remembers people and things from months ago,
        she talks,
        she runs,
            etc., etc. . . .
So—
    where's the retarded?

Look,
    I know she is!
    I just don't know,
        (if she's doing all those same things other kids her age
        are doing),
            just what it is
                that sets her aside
                and qualifies her
                        for a special title.
Is she just a memorizer
                —not a figurer?
Is she just a mimic
                —not capable of conceptualizing?
No, she invents,
        plans,
        schemes,
        cons,
        responds/reacts,
        deals with.

Sometimes she handles life
        like it was her own chess game.
She plans a move
    that will elicit a response
          so she can control a reaction.

So—
    where's the retarded?
        What's the retarded part of her?
    She's retarded,
        but I can't pinpoint *where*,
        I can't define *what*.
She seems to have the basic equipment
          that all the other kids have,
      all the stuff
        that's necessary to life.
So—
    what's the key?
What is it that she's missing
    that will make her
        ever unable
          to do life
            right?
What *defines* her retardation?
What,
    finally,
      will describe
        her lifelong
          delay?

    The inability to theorize?
    The inability to conceptualize?
    The need to always train
        and never coast?
      (Does the retarded mind lose information while resting
        like a pot with a small leak?)

Will it be
      that she just can't keep moving ahead
               on her own,
      that she won't be able to take today's information
              and use it to answer tomorrow's problems
              and make tomorrow's plans?

On the other hand,
    if she *does* have
             all the basic equipment,

can it be expanded to give her
                    all the tools
                              she needs?
Can all her equipment be trained
                    to give her
                              "normal"?
I see her with bright kids her age
and I know she's behind
                              in some things.
And I wonder—
          does she have *enough*
                              of the stuff of life
that with training,
                    she can stay close to the others?

Can we force
          train
          teach
             her
                 into somewhere-near-normal,
     or are there obstacles
                    that she just *won't*
                              be able to hurdle?

I catch myself
          looking
                 for the right answers,
        but I realize
                    that I don't even know
                              the right questions.
What is it, Bethy?
What's the blockage?
Where is it?
Is there blockage?
Is it all in you
          or is some of it
                    in our treatment
                              of you?

(Four and a Half)

If,
according to our faith,
                    love is the most important act of humans,
          if love,
               in the end,
                         surpasses science
                              and philosophy
                                   and art
                         as the key to making our world livable
                                   and our salvation possible,
          if love
               is the key to life,
          then how come kids like you
                              have more of it,
                              handle it better,
                              give it more freely,
               and then
                    we call *you*
                              retarded?

It seems to me
                    that if love is the highest,
                              most intelligent,
                              most curing
                                   act of humanity,
          you kids are the most perfect
                              practitioners
                                   of it.

We (the non-retarded)
     are the ones
                    who seem more comfortable
                                   with venom.
You don't.

In fact,
  unless it's a very special event
        and you've been specially coached,
  we don't hear "Down's" people say,
    "I'll kill that S.O.B."
        or
    "Niggers are no good"
        or
    all those other words
            that spew poison
                into others' lives.
You are open about your feelings,
    and honest about your thoughts
          and appraisals,
    and sometimes those things hurt.
But purposeful venom
        and hate
            aren't normally the products
                of your personalities
    like they are
        of ours.

Maybe, Child,
  we are the retarded ones.

Certainly
    we are retarded
        in the ability to give
            perfect love.

The funnel
　　　　through which our love flows
　　　is blocked by mistrust,
　　　　　　　fear,
　　　　　　　prejudice,
　　　　　　　and a battery of thought-out reasons,
　　　　while yours
　　　　　　　just
　　　　　　　　　flows
　　　　　　　　　　freely.

And those who would deny you life
　　　　　　　　because you are "retarded,"
　　　　　or would prevent your life
　　　　　　　　because you *might be* retarded,
　　　simply
　　　　　don't know you,
　　　　　or don't know how important
　　　　　　　　　your life can be
　　　　　　　　　　to the rest of us.
To try to deny you a place in our presence
　　　　is an unloving,
　　　　　　unintelligent act
　　　　　　　　by less loving people
　　　　　　　　　who would deny your love
　　　　　　　　　　　an entrance.

Those who love less
　　　　have always been threatened
　　　　　　　　by the presence
　　　　　　　　　of those who love more,
　　　　and throughout history
　　　　　　　have tried
　　　　　　　　to erase them.
But, child,
　　　　God always has many more of you
　　　　　　　　to come to us—

hidden in our genes,
fighting,
straining,
waiting
to make your entrance
into our lives.

As the Book says,
"God's ways are not our ways."
God is smarter than we are
and constantly confounds us
by doing brilliant
and loving things
like sending kids like *you*
to be the example
of the best God has to offer
—love.

Yet with all its faults,
humanity seems to be somewhat
educable.
So there's hope
that someday
we will look at you,
then look at us,
compare our love,
and finally discover
which of us
is really
retarded.

January, 1981 (Four and a Half Years)

Listening to your endless chatter,
                              it just dawned on me
              that something wonderful
                            has happened to you
                                    these last couple of months.

All last summer
                    when you rambled on at the mouth,
              people looked at me
                            to interpret
                                your meanings.

I could usually understand
                    the first,
                    and the last word
                                of each statement,
              but I'd have to guess
                            the rest.

Today I discovered
                    that I understood
                                almost every word!

You are moving, Kid!
        And Melanie's speech therapy
                        is paying off big!

"Hey, Pickle, gimme a kiss."
                                "No, not now, I beesy."

I often wondered
                if *that*
                    was inherited
                            in women.

Does it eventually become
                    "I've got a headache"?

Kid, you are well on your way
                    to becoming
                              a full-fledged woman.

Abortion
          is a big issue now.
          And it has lots of ramifications
                              for kids like you.
It causes me fears
                    about some people
                    and experiences
                              it would keep
                                   from our world.

The issue of a woman's body
               and control over the life in it
                              is an important issue.
          But it's just the tip
                    of the iceberg.

We all know that lawmakers
                    could never let it go
                              with just
                                   that issue.

We already hear them deciding
          about the kinds of people
                    who should
                    and *shouldn't*
                              be.

And I don't feel that they are smart,
                    kind,
                    civilized,
                    godly,
                    mature,
                    advanced,
                    unselfish
                        enough
                            to make decisions
                                    like that.
None of us are.

In fact, I think
            when history is written
                        5,000 years from now,
        our times will be included
                            as an extension
                                    of the dark ages
            because we still try to solve our problems
                                        by taking away life
                from those who are
                        or who might be
                                problems to us,
        instead of capturing their worth,
                opening their potential,
                curing their problems,
                and growing with the knowledge
                            and experiments
                        that come from loving and wise acts
                        toward the handicapped.

And special gifts like you,
                Kid,
                    could be affected
                            and lost to us
                                    forever.

"If there's a chance that the child will be poor,
                                        unwanted,
                                        abused,
                                        unhappy,"
                                                some say,
                                                        "abort."
Who knows,
            before a child is born,
                        what happiness he will have
                                                —or bring?
Who knows
            what her quality of life will be like
                                        when she is thirty?
Who knows
            what cures will exist?
Child,
            I too fit some of the qualifications for aborting—
            born into a family which certainly couldn't afford me,
                        a family which became desperately poor—
            and my life *has* been worth something
                                        to me
                                                and to others.
"If we know the child will be born deformed
                                or retarded
                                or handicapped . . ."
Beth,
            what they don't realize is
                        that what you have already given us
                                        and taught us
                        is so much more
                                    than you can ever
                                                cost us.
Your brother Matthew couldn't talk
                                or walk,
            but he brought us more pure love
            and he taught us more about life
                        and giving
            than many of the folks who make the rules

that would deny life
       to people like him,
and would deny our world
       of a joy
       and a presence
that it can ill afford to lose.

And I'm not willing to trust decisions on life
       to people who worry about how their decision
       will affect their chances
              for reelection.

"Handicapped . . . retarded . . . It would be better if she didn't live."
    Better for whom?
       her?
         us?
How does removing her kind of love
            make us
              better?
How does erasing the challenge of a life like hers
              make us
                better?

Why would it be *better*?
    Because she's not like others?
        No one is!
    Because she's not as bright as others?
        There was only one Einstein,
            one Schweitzer,
            one Beethoven,
            one Jesus.
        Should the lesser of us die?
How should we decide which point of the I.Q. is too low
            for a valid life?   40?
                                        50?
                                        70?
                                        71?
                                        72?

What if we measured wrong?
What if we don't have the right system?
How do we know,
        before her birth,
            what the measurement will be?
How do we decide which deformity
    makes them
        unworthy
            of our civilization?

What about people who get deformities
                    after they've been here
                                        for awhile?
        Do they *then* become
                        as unworthy of life
                                as they would have been
                    if we had discovered the deformity
                                before they were born?

Look at us.
Humanity's history of deciding death
                        is a history of bad decisions,
                                    selfish motives,
                                    and injustices.
            Jesus
                    Socrates
                            Joan of Arc
                            Blacks
                                Kennedy
                                    King Jr.
                                        Dachau.
We simply aren't good at it.
        We aren't ready yet
                        to make those decisions.
        Who lives?
        Who dies?
Bethy,
the "Mouse,"
Me?
We all fit into categories
                        considered
                                    acceptable for death
                                            before life begins.
Please be careful.
        You may throw away someone
                who could have given the world
                                    more
                                        than *you* did.

(Five Years)

OK—
    a big question—
now that this book
        is coming to its conclusion:
  do I dare let her read it
        as she
           gets older?
It's no problem
      right now.
While she's young,
       it's fun for her to know
          that there's a book
              about her,
         and I can select from it
            what she
              can hear.
        I can pick the poems
            that say love
              and fun.
But what about later
        when she learns to read?
      She knows this is "Beffie's book"
           —a book about her.
What about the poems
        that ask questions
        and say doubts
          that she's not ready to deal with
          and maybe never will be?
Will these words hurt her?
      Will they cause her
        to doubt herself,
        or pressure her
          into giving up
            on some aspect
              of her life?

How will she feel
          about the constant references to her
                    as "retarded"?
How will she feel
          about so many strangers
                  having access
                        to her life?
What if she wants
          to hide her retardation
                  as much as possible?
What if she wants to,
          but can't escape,
                  this book?
Do I have to worry more
          about what I've said
                  in love,
      than about what thoughtless people
                  will have said
                in ignorance
                    or hate?

Will explaining to her
      that I only mean love,
      and that I want to help other parents
                  of kids like her,
      and that I want that part of the world
          that sees kids like her
               as *strange*
        to begin to see them in *love*,
will *that* explaining be enough
          to make this book
                  OK with her?
Will it make her proud
          and warm?
Or will the attention of it
          cause her problems
               the rest
               of her life?
I must be aware of her future feelings.

I must be aware of the possible good this book can be
                                    for others like her,
                                    and for parents like us.
But I hope that
               the love tone
                         that we have already set
            will continue to buffer her
                         through the future
                                    of what good or bad
                a book like this
                         might do
                            to her life.

Bethy,
      I think you understand
                  how we feel.
      I think you already know
            that you have brought us joy
                            and love
                                and fun
                                    and more purpose,
            and that you have strengthened our faith.

And we hope we have done the same
                                    for you.
Together, child,
            we have helped
                  to make each other
                              whole.

To All Who Work with the Handicapped!

My hope for you, my friends,
                         is this:
Each night when you look back at the labors of your day,
      may you go to sleep
                  with smiles on your faces,
                  and memories of small victories
                              in your hearts.
      May the warm moments
                  you have given parents and children
        return to you
        and keep all the chills
                  from your body and soul.
May the things you have poured
        into the oceans of our lives—
            hope,
                joy,
                    a clearer tomorrow,
                  confidence,
                    skills,
                        small successes that cheer us,
                      love,
                          encouragement—
may all of these things come back to you
                and engulf your lives
                  on each returning tide.
      May the things you give us
                  and our children
                    surround *your* lives.
In lonely moments,
      may you remember
             the hugs
                  of small arms,
             the admiration
                  of small eyes,

and the bright and learning faces
that look to *you*
for instruction.

In moments when you wonder if it all adds up,
may you remember the success that you saw
and lived,
but didn't know how to write
into the proper spaces
on the proper forms.
If I had two gifts to give you,
they would be—
the ability to see where our children would have been
if they hadn't had *you*,
and a good memory,
so that each night,
as the day begins to leave your senses,
you remember—
and go to sleep
with smiles on your faces,
and small victories in your hearts.

INFANT DEVELOPMENT CENTER

INDIVIDUAL PROGRAM PLAN—STAFF EVALUATION

Child's Name: Bethany Bakely   Entry Date: 7-15-76
DOB: 6-14-76   IPP Conference Date: 5-19-81
Coordinator: Recorder: Lee Ann Britain
Persons Attending -
    Child's Family: Jeanne and Donald Bakely (Parents)
    IDC Staff: Barbara Lawrence (Preschool Teacher), Lee Ann Britain (Director)

Assessments:
    C.A. 4 yrs. 11 mos.

                                                        Gain in 6 mos.

Language	4 yrs. scattered to 5	
Social	Within normal limits	
Self-help feeding	Within normal limits	
Self-help toileting	Within normal limits	
Self-help dressing	not tested	
Cognition	5½ yrs.	
Fine Motor	5 yrs.	¾ yr.
Gross Motor	4½ yrs.	

Parents' Concern:

Long Term Goal: Placement in public school program Sept. 1981.

Short Term Goal: For summer, recommend continuation of alphabet identification, number concepts 1-10 and continuation of number identification 1-20. Beth should be encouraged to write her name using upper and lower case letters. Suggest Beth work on address and telephone number understanding in preparation for school.

Plan: Terminate IDC Program in May. Attend local school system in Fall of 1981.
Your signature indicates you have participated in this conference regarding your child.
Parent's Signature: Jeanne F. Bakely   Date: May 19, 1981
Parent's Signature: Donald C. Bakely   Date: May 19, 1981

cc: Parents   Mr. Teeples - Wy. Co. Coop.

Update - September 1981

This month, Bethany Flagg Bakely did it!
She entered kindergarten in the Kansas City, Kansas, public school system.
She did it at the normal age, in regular classes — just like any other kid.
As far as we know, she's the first Down's syndrome child to do this in Kansas history.
She loves it!
The tone set by her teacher, Mrs. Emma Smith, has helped her be a natural part of her class, accepted and loved by the other children.
We are grateful to the Major Hudson Elementary School staff for taking a chance with Beth, and for making school such a good experience for her.
(Get ready, teachers. There are a lot more "Beths" heading your way. You are in for a neat challenge, and a great experience. You have the opportunity to make a real difference in the lives of a lot of handicapped children. Go with it! It's going to be worth it!)

Matthew David Bakely

March 10, 1960

September 7, 1965

Writing this is a very hard thing
                    for me—
        partly because I have lost too much of him
                            from my head
        and partly because the things I remember
                are the things
                        that touched me most deeply
                        and affected me the most.
Often,
        when I begin to fill pages with him,
                        I stop.
Something in me cries,
                "I can't do this."
                "I don't want to live
                        through this again."
                "I don't want to feel his pain,
                    see his tears,
                    hear his screams,
                    or watch him die
                            —again."
I have already gone through that once—
                            in fact,
                                too many times,
        and it was finally going away.

I think,
        "Those who read this are strangers
        —people who have no right
                        to want me to do this for them."
I think,
        "I can't possibly owe *them*,
                    what writing this
                            does
                                to me."
But then,
        there's the other side.

I *do* write.
 And when I do,
    I get to see his face again—
 those big,
   always-saying-something eyes,
 that gushy mouth,
 that nothin' nose.

And writing and thinking,
 I get to feel
   that sweet, skinny body
     against mine,
   those scrawny fingers
     squeezing mine.
 I hear the laughter,
 see all that effort,
 watch the family loving him together,
 and
  it's
   good.

And I'm reminded
  that I owe *me*
   him, again.
  I need him.
   And so do *you*.
God made him
 to be known.
  And this is the way
    you
    get to know him.
God made him
 to be remembered.
And this is the way
  I
  get to remember him.

This is the way
        I
           get to hold my son
                again.
And
    it's OK
       to bring him back
          —for you
         and for me.

I missed his birth by a couple of hours.
                  (This was normal for me.)
Jeanne was trying to be brave,
    but finally it came out:
              "I think something is the matter
              with the baby."
We had a little warning,
             but not enough to tell us any certainties.
        —Jeanne had eaten some spoiled chicken
           while on a camping trip
              during the second month of pregnancy,
               and the poisoning was intense.
        —This baby didn't seem as active in the womb
           as the first four.

The first thing that struck me,
                  when I went to see him,
    was that he had dark hair,
              like his mother.
    (All the rest were light,
             like me.)
Finally, I thought,
         one for Jeanne.

Then I saw
    what she saw.

The head was distorted,
            flat in the back,
                        like a chunk underneath the skull
                                    was missing.
There was just
            a whole different look
                        about him.
My heart sank.
      What are you supposed
                        to *do*
                        about something
                                    like this?

I wasn't repulsed.
      I was just confused
                        about what the next step
                                    should be.
      I never have had much
                  of a panic point.
      My mind almost always
                  looks
                        for the next move.
I remember thinking,
            "Well, we can't tell yet
                              exactly
                              what the problem is,
      so some decisions
                  have to be
                        delayed."
And I thought,
            "Whoever this is
                        that God gave us this time
      must be someone God loves
                        and we are to love him, too.

After all,
      God has been in business
                  a long time.

God seems to know
what he's doing.
And anyway,
God seems to make decisions
without checking with me
first."
I felt there was a reason
that this child
was sent into our lives.
We'd just have to find out why,
and decide what to do,
as we went along.

I returned to Jeanne
and tried to be cute.
"The first four looked just like me.
The first time one looks like you,
you want to call a specialist."
Then,
"Yeah, Honey,
something *is* wrong.
You can see it just by looking.
Anyway,
the nurses all had it
in their eyes."
So,
Matthew David Bakely—soon to be known as the "Mouse"
was born to us.
And a whole new dimension
was thrown
into our lives.
And a whole new, wonderful experience
was beginning
for us.

They loved us.
They meant well.
One of the elderly women at the church
    came to me
        soon after the "Mouse" was born:
    "We hear there's something the matter
                with your baby.
    We share your pain.
    We are praying
        that this burden
            will be lifted from you.
    We are praying
        that your baby will die."
We loved them.
We knew they meant well.
But they came from a different age,
        a different frame of reference.
    "Please don't," we said.
    "You'll put God in a terrible spot.
        We are praying
        that
            he
                will
                    live!"

The guitar
        was his favorite instrument,
    but that's because the guitar
                was what I played
      and I
        was his favorite
            dad.
Each night, after supper,
           and before my church meetings began,
    I would take him up to my bedroom,
        lay him on the bed,
        practice on my guitar,
        and sing my way all through a "simple songs for beginners" book.
He loved it.
    (He was about the only one who did.)
Noises were a special sensation to him
    and if there was *anything*
              I offered with that guitar
                it was noise.
If *you* want to plink and sing,
           here's a couple of quick lessons.
    If you are a good player,
        play loud and sing quiet.
    If you are a rotten player,
        sing loud to drown out the guitar.
    If you are a rotten player *and* singer,
           take your retarded kid
        (borrow one if you don't have one)
           close the door,
           and play and sing your heart out.
Look—
    the kid's a captive audience
        (especially if he can't walk)
    a non-critic
        (especially if he can't talk)
    he probably enjoys the noise
        and you need the time
           together.

Most hats are built to fit snugly
                        on fairly round
                                heads.
Now,
        if you looked down
                        on the "Mouse's" head
                and saw his head as a clock
                                with his nose as the 12,
        you would see a fairly decent circle
                                from the 7 to the 4
                but from the 4 to the 7,
                                it was a kind of straight,
                                        flat
                                        line.
They don't make hats
                        for heads like that!

But winters
        and rains
                and dress-up times
                        come to "Matthews"
                                as well as to others.
And sometimes kids like him
                        need hats.

Trying hats on Matthew
                        in a department store
                was often done with some of our other kids in tow,
                and was one of the last great
                                pure forms
                                        of entertainment.

We would try
        hard hats
            baseball caps
                dress hats with feathers
                    fur-lined hoods
                        rain hats
                            shower caps
                                football helmets
                                    baby caps
                                        cowboy hats
                                            and derbys.

And they would
        tilt to the back
                tilt to the front
                        tilt to the side
                                fall down over his eyes
                                        fall down over his ears
                                                and sometimes over his chin
                                        and do anything
                                                but stay on right.
We would
        tie them
                sew on elastic straps
                        stuff the flat spot with hankies
                                or fill the hat with paper
                                        to make it only fall down far enough
                                        so he could still see
                                                and hear.
He'd push his head against the high back of his chair,
        dislodge his hat,
                        which would fall down over his nose,
        and he would giggle.
He'd sneak his head past the restraining guards of his chair,
        his head would flop down,
        his hat would snap off
                        and fall to the floor,
        and he would giggle.
Finding a soft hat
                with an elastic head band,
                with no stiff-parts-that-a-floppy-head-could-bump-
                into-things-with-to-knock-the-hat-loose,
                in his size,
                which looked good,
                and didn't emphasize his distortion,
                                wasn't easy.
But it
        sure
                was
                        fun!

When the street gangs accepted the "Mouse"
                                        as a part of their lives,
            it was only
                        partly
                        a blessing.
They loved him half to death—
                        which was good.
They protected him from harm—
                        which was good—and bad.
It was like having him surrounded with guard dogs.
If a stranger,
            even at church,
                        looked at him oddly,
            they wanted to do the stranger
                                some exquisite harm.
I had to remind the "hoods"
                        that Matthew *looked* different.
                        His handicap was noticeable.
            It was natural for people to look at him
                                        with curiosity.
"After all,"
            I explained,
                        "That's how *you* looked at him
                                        at first."
It took a while,
                        but they finally learned
            not to take offense
                        at those who stared
                                at their little friend.
I often found them
            patiently explaining Matthew's predicament
                                in their own inimitable style
            to anyone who needed
                        —or didn't need—
                                the education.
Gradually,
            through the "Mouse,"
                        they learned

that kindness to Matthew,
          who was retarded,
     should be extended to others
          who were also retarded—
  retarded in their information
    and acceptance
      of kids like him
        —and like them.

We tried to analyze
     his strength
     and coordination.

It seemed to us
    that he was strongest nearest his head,
      and weakest nearest his feet;
    that he was better coordinated up top,
      and got less coordinated toward the bottom.

So even though he couldn't control chewing,
    his mouth was still the best coordinated
             part of him.

If it was open,
    we often played a game
        called
         "Mousetrap."
We would touch his tongue
      with a finger.
The touch signaled his mouth
      to close
        with the speed
        and the force
          of a mousetrap.

Same speed.
Same pain.

The finger had to get out immediately.
If it didn't
and the finger got caught in the teeth,
it was no longer a game
to the owner of the finger.
Anything that got in his mouth
got bit.
Always.
During these days,
Lois was an infant,
still crawling.
Matthew often lay on the floor,
another object in her path.

Once, instead of crawling around him
she crawled right over his tummy.
He giggled.
But on the way over him,
her hand got in his mouth
and touched his tongue.
He, of course, bit.
The shock of it
was more overwhelming
than the pain.
(After all,
other objects didn't bite her
when she crawled over them.)
She quickly got off,
sat up,
and looked at this person
who caused her pain.
Her bottom lip popped out,
a few tears came,
and she thought about it.

Then she went back to him,
                grabbed his hand,
                        and bit him back.

He looked at this person
                who caused him pain.
        His bottom lip popped out,
                his eyes watered,
                        he thought about it,
                                and giggled.

His biting
        seemed
                uncontrollable.

        Anything that got near his mouth got bit
                                hard,
                                        immediately—
                —his own hand,
                        or mine,
                                or anything that got within range.
He didn't seem capable
                of *not*
                        biting.
He had tremendous force in his jaws.

Feeding him
        was a lesson
                in patience.
He would bite the spoon
                and we couldn't
                        pull it out.

We would wiggle it carefully
　　　　so as not to damage his teeth
　　　　and talk to him
　　　　　　to take his concentration
　　　　　　　　off the bite.
Eventually we would get the spoon out,
　　　　　only to have to do it all over again.
Soft foods,
　　　ground up,
　　　　　already digestible,
　　　　　　were all he could eat.
Biting worked;
　　　chewing didn't.
　　　　　Feeding took a while.

He had a certain chilling scream
　　　that signaled
　　　　　a bite on his hand
　　　　　　in the process.
He knew that it was going to happen.
He knew that there was nothing he could do about it.

That scream
　　　was the scream
　　　　　of anticipated agony.
　　　　　　On the way.
　　　　　　Unwelcome.
At that scream,
　　　everyone rushed toward him.
And we would see the thumb
　　　　on the way
　　　　　to the mouth—
his whole existence trying
　　　to force it away.
His mind screaming to his hand,
　　　　don't!
His mind ordering his mouth,
　　　　bite!

His eyes watching,
                    panic stricken
                              with pain on the way
          helpless to stop the process.

Sometimes we got there in time
          and wrestled his hand away.
Sometimes we got there too late.
          The thumb was in.
          The sharp teeth
                    had made their goal
                              through the skin
                              right to the bone.
          The blood and pain
                              were almost more than we
                                        (and he)
                                        could bear.
          His mind screamed to this thumb,
                              get out!
          His mind screamed to this teeth,
                              hold on!
          His teeth
               always
                    won.
Getting his thumb out
          was a work of art.
It had to be done quickly
                    without doing more damage
                              to his hand
          or causing him too much more pain.
I would wedge my thumbs
                    into the opening between his teeth
                    on either side of his trapped thumb,
          and twist slowly,
               but forcibly,
          until his teeth opened far enough
                              for his thumb to pop out.

The tears would continue
　　while his whole body
　　　　　went from shaking stiff
　　　　　　　　to limp.
Understand—
　　　　　it wasn't something he got used to.
It didn't hurt him less than it would hurt you.
　　(Try biting your finger hard enough to break the skin,
　　and you get a small idea of what he went through
　　several times a day.)

For a while,
　　　　　his hand looked like diseased hamburger.
We tried everything—
　　We tied his hand to the chair,
　　　　but he hated it.
　　We pinned his sleeve to his pants leg.
　　　　but he worked his arm out.

Finally, while patching up one of his many wounds,
　　Dr. Warwick (one of the world's most *decent* men),
　　　　　suggested a cast
　　　　　　　for his elbow.
　　It was the answer.

He could still move his arm,
　　　　　　　　but not bend his elbow.
We would hear the scream
　　that announced the hand
　　　　　　on the way to his mouth,
　　rush to him,
　　and watch the stiffened arm
　　　　　　　move the thumb
　　　right past his face,
　　　　　　never able to get it into his mouth.
And the grateful,
　　　relieved smile
　　　　　would just fill
　　　　　　his face.

"Hey, Bake, let's go!"
I used to hate
    driving the kids from the street gangs
        on their trips.
To get where we were going,
    we always had to pass through downtown.
The kids would hang out the windows,
    say bad things to people,
    throw things at people on the sidewalk,
    and do all kinds of nasty stuff.
The van had our church's name printed on the sides.
    All this didn't help our image.

One day,
    while baby-sitting the "Mouse,"
    I found I had to drive the Pythons
        (they were as sweet as their name)
        to the "Y" on the other side of town.
I got them into the van
    handed the "Mouse" to the worst of them
    and said,
        "Hold him,
        I can't drive and hold him at the same time."
The kid grumbled,
    but held him.
This time,
    as we passed through the downtown,
    it suddenly dawned on me
        that they weren't hollering
        or throwing things.
I looked in the rearview mirror
    to see what was going *right*.
As I watched,
    I saw that they were all
        absorbed
        in Matthew.
They were taking turns
    holding him,

kissing his cheeks,
rubbing noses,
and being gentle
with no shame
or embarrassment.
The *Pythons*—the most vicious gang we ever worked with!

As I watched,
it dawned on me what was happening.
For the first time
in some of their lives
someone needed them.
And it was a new and wonderful experience.

A few weeks later,
after a particularly tense time between the Gladiators
and the Pythons,
I finally got both gangs to make a temporary truce,
and sent them on their way.

The head of the Pythons didn't leave.
He didn't seem hostile.
It just seemed as though he had something
he wanted to say.
It was awkward for a moment,
but, finally,
he made his move.
"You remember that time you let me hold your kid?
Well, I just wanted to tell you
that was the first time I can ever remember
taking another human body
and squeezing it right next to mine
without being smacked
punched,
cussed,
or shoved away.
"Thanks.
I know it wasn't easy for you

                                    to let kids like us
                                      hold him."
I saw his eyes start to cloud
        and he quickly got out
                        before he allowed himself the luxury
                            of another human,
                                        vulnerable
                                          emotion.
My Lord,
            what have we done to him?
What is it like to be fifteen,
        and never be able to remember touching anyone
                                in love?
                        or having anyone touch *you*
                                in love?
And who else but a "Matthew"
        could have allowed him
                    that one moment
                            of tender humanness?
Matthew
        couldn't
                shove him away.
        His body didn't
                do
                    shoves.
Matthew didn't
            distinguish
                between people
                    deserving
                    or undeserving
                        of love.
        He was happy to get hugged
                    by anybody
                and to give love
                        to anybody.

Often those who look
            like they can only take,

may have much to give
and important things to offer
                    to those who need.

OK, Matthew,
        we're gonna' march!

Usually it was Steve (about eleven years old)
        who got the progression moving.

The six kids,
        parents,
                and whoever else was hanging around,
        all lined up
                for homemade physical therapy.

At the thought of it,
                Matthew's face
                and body
                        came alive—
                                giggly
                                quivering
                                jumping with
                                        excitement.
I held Matthew's body up
                supported by his hands.
I lifted his right leg off the ground
        by pulling his right arm up
                high enough
                        for that to happen.

Then I lifted the left.
                  Then the right—
           trying to teach him the motion of walking
               of a foot lifting,
                             then going down to contact the floor,
              followed by the other foot
                   doing the same.
We went single file.
The kids were playing imaginary instruments—
                          trombones,
                          flutes,
                          cymbals,
                          drums,
                          and whatever else
                                struck their fancy.
Noise,
     music,
          cadence,
               shouts of encouragement,
                    laughing,
                        cheers,
        around the living room,
               down the street,
                 across the park.
It *did* attract attention,
    but the neighbors understood,
               encouraged,
               joined in,
               enjoyed this effort
                     to teach a boy
                       to walk.
And he *tried*.
    His mind wanted so badly
               to make his legs
                  take
                    their own steps.

Even we
    could feel the strain
        and see his desire
                to do this
                    simple thing.
We knew he had no balance.
We knew his body couldn't control
                    standing up,
                    supporting himself.
When we tried,
        he just collapsed—
                giggling.
The strength was there;
    the ability to control was not.
But we felt that if he could learn
                to make stepping movements,
    someday the balance and control
                might come too,
                    and get together.
And anyway,
    he needed small touches of success,
    and we needed to be trying something
                —anything—
    and we needed this special time with him,
                    and he with us.

One day, as we were lining up for the march
                and passing out the imaginary musical instruments,
    we saw it come over him.
Something started to click
            in his mind.

He,
    by himself,
    on his own,
    at his own initiative,
    on purpose,
    by his own control,

lifted his right foot off the ground,
put it down again,
and,
    of course,
        giggled.
And he *knew* that he did it!
We cheered
    and we laughed,
        and we hugged him
            and patted his back,
                and told him how proud we were.
    And he was proud, too.

It was then that we knew
    that *he* knew
        what we were trying to get him to do.
    He understood!

It was an awkward step, of course.

He was so lanky and disjointed
    that he hit himself in the mouth
                with his knee.
The look of surprise on his face
                made us laugh so hard
    that we almost lost sight
            of what had really happened.
Then Claudia said,
        "He did it!"
And the joy
    erupted!

He did it after that, too.
That right leg would go up and down,
    and we would shout him on.

Finally the day came
        when he did the right,
                then the left,
    and we knew that he was on his way.

We didn't care
        for ourselves
           if it took forty years
                to get him to walk.
He was on his way
        and we were on the way with him.

Being a family
        active in the church,
    we naturally had lots of meetings
            where there were lots of people.
We wanted Matthew
        to be exposed to people,
    and we wanted people
        exposed to him.

So we took Matthew into lots of different settings.
    (We couldn't very well leave him at home to answer the phone.)

Some folks at the meetings knew him,
        loved him,
        and dealt with him wonderfully.

Some folks at the meetings knew us
                    and accepted him
                                    because of *that*.
But there were those
                    to whom he was strange
          and who often reacted
                              in accord with that feeling.

They would shy away from him,
              or be repulsed,
              or just be uncomfortable.

I would make a point
                  of getting acquainted
                                  with those folks
          so that they'd be comfortable
                        with me.
Then I'd bide my time
          and at the right moment
                      talk to them
                                  with Matthew in my arms.
I'd make an excuse to leave for a moment
          and nonchalantly ask them
                          to hold Matthew for me.
They couldn't very well refuse,
          and they couldn't hold him for very long
                      without feeling differently
                                      about him.
And often they became
          some of the folks who knew him,
                      and loved him,
                      and dealt wonderfully with him,
                      and ended up bragging
              that they were one of the ones
                              who were allowed to hold him.

To the Hospital Worker Who Held Him as He Died

He had been sick
        for so long.
For two weeks
        the hospital could get no nourishment
                into his body.
For days and nights
        we held his frail weakening body
        and watched his painful crying
           become a weak, tearless whimper.
At nights we would go home
        and fall exhausted in our bed
              and
                in our anguish.
The night he died
        was another
           of *those* nights.

We were at home in fitful sleep,
      hoping that the next day of holding him
            would be the day
      when his condition would turn around
        and start him
           on the road to health again.
So
    we weren't there
        when he died.
We weren't there
        when his eyes and heart
           needed our faces to say good-bye to.
We weren't there
        when his soul leapt free
           from his useless body,
        when he finally stood—
           stood!
        on his own!
           before God's throne.

We weren't there
　　　　when our son's heart
　　　　　　could no longer fight back
　　　　　　　　the overpowering force of death,
　　　　when it finally coughed
　　　　　　　　　　its last cough,
　　　　and it simply
　　　　　　whisked him
　　　　　　　　away from us.
We weren't there
　　　　at that special moment of his need
　　　　　　to hold him tight
　　　　　　　　as we tried to squeeze the fear out of him
　　　　　　　　　　　　　and out of us.
We weren't there.
　　　　But,
　　　　　　thank God,
　　　　　　　　you were!
I don't know if we ever heard your name.
I don't know if we ever told you of our gratitude.
His death
　　　　seemed to blot out
　　　　　　　all other happenings
　　　　　　　　　information
　　　　　　　　　concerns
　　　　　　　　　　　that night.
Our minds,
　　　　our hearts,
　　　　　　were on overload.

But we've thought of you since,
　　　and thanked God for your kindness
　　　　　　　　many times.
They tell us that when Matthew died
　　　you were holding him
　　　　　　　in your arms.
Your shift at the hospital
　　　　　　had long been over.

But you stayed late
                just to hold our boy.
And he died
                in your arms.
Because of you,
                special woman,
        he was able to move
                from the warmth and love
                                of your lap and arms,
                from the security
                        of seeing your face
                        and hearing your calming voice
                directly to the warmth and love
                                of the lap of God
                without a break
                                in loving.
Right now,
        I can't recall your name,
                                but
                        God
                                can.

And I'm sure God's memory
                        is better
                                than mine.
From what I've heard
                and read
                        about God,
        it cheers his heart
                to see you give
                        your love.
I don't know
        if you will ever see this book
                or feel our thanks,
        but to all of you who give your love
                while you give your skills,
                                thank you!

You have done more than you know for us,
   for you made the transition
      from life to Life
            a warm one
                 for our son
  when we weren't there.

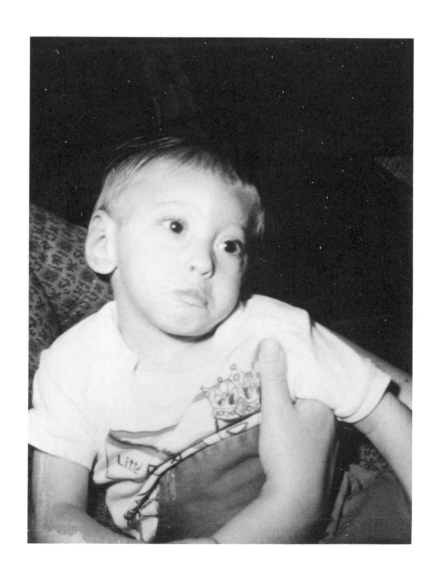

I feel just a little silly,
      a little strange,
      a little theologically unsound,
    standing here by your grave
           trying to bring you up to date
                on your family.
But I'm human, Son,
          and humans seem to function better
    when they've got something solid
           to feel
             and to see.
    And this piece of ground
           is where I saw them put you last.

Boy,
    it's me,
      your dad.
And I just wanted to tell you,
      to remind you,
        for your sake
          —and mine—
           that I still love you,
      and that the loving
        and remembering can't be stopped
          —hardly even dimmed—
           by a thing called death.
Right now,
    the thing I feel
        is the pain
        and the love together
  all twisting up my insides
  and making this moment,
      this act,
        so very hard for me.

I'm never sure that I can stand this.
  And I wonder
    if you can.

I keep wondering
             if you sense me here—
             if this act,
                      this gesture,
                               makes any difference to you
                                        right now.
I almost feel your little body jump
             your little face explode in joy,
                               the way it did years ago
        when I would come home at night
                      to touch you.
Oh, God,
    how I miss you!
If you only knew how I want to dismiss those years
        between now
                 and that day
        when your body and heart
                      could no longer deal with life.

I wouldn't want you to go back to that kind of living again, Son,
        but I sure would like a chance
                      to go through it again
                               with you.
I need you, Boy.
             I always did.
And I'm grateful—so grateful
                      to the God who was wise enough
        to give you to us
                 even for such a short,
                          blessed,
                          agonizing
                               time.
And I'm grateful
             even for times like this
        —times that hurt—
             but times when I can still see your face
                               and scrawny fingers
                                        in my heart

and when I can feel your soul
          and your joy
              touching me again.
The want
      wrenches me.

I want to hold that squiggly body
      and touch my nose to yours,
      and giggle at the funny words
              your eyes said,
      and flip your body over on the bed,
      and watch you respond to my guitar
              and the singing.
I *want*!!
      Oh, God, how I want
          and pain
             to be your holder again.
But I can't. . .
      not for the rest
          of a lifetime.
Oh!!
   God damn death!!
   God damn it for the separation it causes!
God damn death
      for ripping you from this father's arms!
God damn death
      for keeping me from your face
      for keeping me from those fingers
             that wrapped around mine!
God damn death
      for no longer letting me
           hug the pain
           and crying
             out of you!
God damn death
      for burning its way into simple human minds
          not really equipped to deal with it!

God damn death
        for this five feet of separation
                which might as well be a million miles!
God damn death!!

He did . . . didn't he?
That's what the cross
        and the resurrection
                are all about.
Son,
    I know that your resurrection already is.
You are free from the body that trapped you.

You run
    and talk
    and laugh
    and do the things your heart wanted to do
        but your body wouldn't let you.

God *did* damn death
        and because of him,
                death stops being death
             and only becomes a wait
                    for me.
Death/separation *forever*
        seems
            unspeakable cruelty,
    but death/separation *until*—
                I can live with *that*!

Yes, Son,
    I *can* live with that
        until I find *my* resurrection
                and see you again,
    and that certainly takes the bite
        out of death.

I love you, Son,
   and death
     can't do beans
      about that!
Love has a way
   of jumping chasms
  and love
   doesn't have
     to wait.

The sad part is this:
  even if our society
     could
      invent people,
   neither Bethy
    nor the "Mouse"
     would have even been considered as options.
  And look what we'd
    have
     missed.

Donald C. Bakely was born in a small town in New Jersey, the fourth of six children. While he was in grammar school, his family lived in poverty and Don had his first brushes with the law. After an undistinguished high school career, Don enlisted in the paratroopers, serving in North Carolina, Georgia, New York, and Alabama.

In 1948 Don heard the call to preach and was accepted at West Virginia Wesleyan College where he attended for one year. He then served as assistant pastor of the Centenary Tabernacle Methodist Church in Camden, New Jersey. While studying at Temple University where he received a B.S. in education and a M.Div., he served two other Camden churches.

In 1958 Don was called to return to Centenary Tabernacle in Camden, this time as its pastor. This church had dropped in membership from over seven hundred to seventy, as the neighborhood changed economically and racially. Don's work included work with neighborhood youth who were involved in gangs.

In 1965 Don, his wife Jeanne, and their six children moved to Kansas City where he became executive director of Cross-Lines Cooperative Council. Cross-Lines helps people of different races and religious backgrounds pool their resources to meet problems caused by poverty and ignorance. Backed by several hundred churches of over thirty denominations, Cross-Lines involves many volunteers in projects that deal with housing, health, legal aid, recreation, community organization, job training, etc.

Because the ideas of Cross-Lines are workable in rural, city, and suburban areas, Rev. Bakely speaks on the average of two hundred to three hundred times a year across the nation to national, regional, and local groups interested in using their resources to meet community needs. He has received special commendations from President Ford, from the national Jaycees and many state Jaycee chapters as well as from other state and local groups. He was the recipient of the Liberty Bell Award from the American Bar Association and a life membership to PTA.

His first book, *If . . . a Big Word with the Poor*, was free verse with photographs by Terry Evans, a Salina, Kansas, photographer. Don is currently working on another book about Cross-Lines, poverty, and inner-city work.